MATHS & ENGLISH FOR
HAIRDRESSING
Graduated exercises and practice exam

Andrew Spencer and Habia

CENGAGE
Learning·

Australia • Brazil • Japan • Korea • Mexico • Singapore • Spain • United Kingdom • United States

Maths & English for Hairdressing
Andrew Spencer and Habia

Publishing Director: Linden Harris

Commissioning Editor: Lucy Mills

Development Editor: Claire Napoli

Production Editor: Alison Cooke

Production Controller: Eyvett Davis

Marketing Manager: Lauren Mottram

Typesetter: Cenveo Publisher Services

Cover design: HCT Creative

For product information and technology assistance, contact **emea.info@cengage.com**.

For permission to use material from this text or product, and for permission queries, email **emea.permissions@cengage.com**.

This work is Adapted from Pre Apprenticeship: Maths & Literacy Series by Andrew Spencer, published by Cengage Learning Australia Pty Limited © 2010.

British Library Cataloguing-in-Publication Data
A catalogue record for this book is available from the British Library.

ISBN: 978-1-4080-7267-7

Cengage Learning EMEA
Cheriton House, North Way, Andover, Hampshire, SP10 5BE, United Kingdom

Cengage Learning products are represented in Canada by Nelson Education Ltd.

For your lifelong learning solutions, visit **www.cengage.co.uk**

Purchase your next print book, e-book or e-chapter at **www.cengagebrain.com**

Printed in Malta by Melita Press
1 2 3 4 5 6 7 8 9 10 – 14 13 12

Maths & English for Hairdressing

Contents

Introduction   v
About the authors   vi
Acknowledgements   vi

ENGLISH

Unit 1	Spelling	1
Unit 2	Alphabetizing	4
Unit 3	Comprehension	6
Unit 4	Homophones	12
Unit 5	Writing Letters and Emails	15
Unit 6	Format, Style and Interpreting Data	19
Unit 7	Grammar and Punctuation	23

MATHEMATICS

Unit 8	General Mathematics	25
Unit 9	Basic Operations Section A: Addition Section B: Subtraction Section C: Multiplication Section D: Division	29
Unit 10	Decimals Section A: Addition Section B: Subtraction Section C: Multiplication Section D: Division	34
Unit 11	Fractions Section A: Addition Section B: Subtraction Section C: Multiplication Section D: Division	39
Unit 12	Percentages and Ratios Section A: Percentages Section B: Ratios	42

Unit 13	Measurement Conversions	45
Unit 14	Time	47
Unit 15	Earning Wages	48
Unit 16	Squaring Numbers	50
	Section A: Introducing square numbers	
	Section B: Applying square numbers to the trade	
Unit 17	Vouchers	52
Unit 18	Deals	55
Unit 19	Industry Related Maths	57
Unit 20	Practice Written Exam for the Hairdressing Industry	62

Hairdressing Glossary 71
Maths and English Glossary 73
Formulae and Data 74
Times Tables 75
Multiplication Grid 76
Online Answer Guide 77
Notes 79

Introduction

It has always been important to understand, from a teacher's perspective, the nature of the maths and English skills students need for their future, rather than teaching them textbook mathematics. This has been a guiding principle behind the development of the content in this workbook. To teach maths and English that is *relevant* to students seeking apprenticeships is the best that we can do, to give students an education in the field that they would like to work in.

The content in this resource is aimed at the level that is needed for a student to have the best possibility of improving their maths and English skills specifically for Hairdressing. Students can use this workbook to prepare for their functional skills assessment, or even to assist with basic maths and English for their Hairdressing and Barbering qualification. This resource has the potential to improve the students' understanding of basic mathematical concepts that can be applied to the Hairdressing industry and salon environment. These resources have been trialled, and they work.

Commonly used industry terms are introduced so that students have a basic understanding of terminology they will encounter in the workplace environment. Students who can complete this workbook and reach a higher outcome in all topics will have achieved the goal of this resource.

The content in this workbook is the first step towards bridging the gap between what has been learnt in previous years, and what needs to be remembered and re-learnt for use in exams and in the workplace. Students will significantly benefit from the consolidation of the basic maths and english concepts.

In many ways, it is a win-win situation, with students enjoying and studying relevant maths and English for Hairdressing and training organizations and employers (RTOs) receiving students that have improved basic maths and English skills.

All that is needed is patience, hard work, a positive attitude, a belief in yourself that you can do it and a desire to achieve. The rest is up to you.

About the authors

Andrew Spencer has studied education both within Australia and overseas. He has a Bachelor of Education, as well as a Masters of Science in which he specialized in teacher education. Andrew has extensive experience in teaching secondary mathematics throughout New South Wales and South Australia for well over 15 years. He has taught a range of subject areas including Maths, English, Science, Classics, Physical Education and Technical Studies. His sense of the importance of practical mathematics continued to develop with the range of subject areas he has taught in.

Maths & English for Hairdressing has been adapted by **Habia**, the government appointed sector skills body and industry authority for hair, beauty, nails, spa therapy, barbering and African type hair.

Habia's role is to create the standards that form the basis of all qualifications in hair and beauty including NVQs, SVQs, Apprenticeships, and Foundation degrees, as well as industry codes of practice.

Acknowledgements

Andrew Spencer:
For Paula, Zach, Katelyn, Mum and Dad.
   Many thanks to Mal Aubrey (GTA) and all training organizations for their input.
   To the De La Salle Brothers for their selfless work with all students.
   Thanks also to Dr Pauline Carter for her unwavering support for all maths teachers.
   This is for all students who value learning, who are willing to work hard and who have character … and are characters!

Thank you to Tracey James at Habia for her valuable industry knowledge and hard work to adapt Maths & English for Hairdressing.

Unit 1: Spelling

Short-answer questions

Specific instructions to students

- This is an exercise to help you to identify and correct spelling errors.
- Read the activity below, then answer accordingly.

Spelling Task 1

Read the following passage and identify and correct the spelling errors.

> A sallon opens at 9.00 a.m. on a Saterday morning. The staff arive
> at 8.00 a.m. to begin proparing for a bussy day, as severel cleints are
> getting maried and they are arriving soon to have their hair styled. The
> managor imediately gets the staff to prepare the equipment as the first
> cleint is due in 45 minates. The scisors need stearalizing again as the
> aprentice dropped them on the floor only minutes before. In adision,
> the floor had not been swapt from the previours day as it was a Bank
> Holliday and everyone was grateful for the day off. At 9.00 a.m. the first
> client appers at the salon's doors.

Incorrect words:

_____

_____

Correct words:

_____

_____

Spelling Task 2

Read the following passage and identify and correct the spelling errors.

Hairdressing is an exciting and varied career. You can find yourself cutting, colouring, perming, putting hair up and doing total re-styles on a wide range of cleints. You could progress on to a ranje of advanced services such as hair extensions, colour corective work and advanced colouring techniques, advanced cutting techniques and special ocassion and wedding styles.

You could work in a high street salon, large department store, health spa, hotel, cruse ship, work as a mobile stylist, or even be a prison hairdresser. You may, after gaining some experience, consider opening your own saloon, working as a sales representive for a hair products wholesalers or manufacturers, or even progressing into teeching and assesing within hairdressing education.

To suceed in the hairdressing industry, it is important to have an aproachable and frendly manner, the ability to put clients at eaze, be diplomatic, tactfull, a good listner and communicator, have a high standard of personal grooming and a comercial awareness with the abillity to sell products and earn commission. The hairdressing industry is closely related to that of fashion, so it is really important to keep up to date with all celebritty and fashion news and styles. You could even find yourself styling hair for fashion shoots for magazines.

Hairdressing offers an endless number of exciting opportunitys and possibilities; it is up to you to make this career your pasport to success.

Incorrect words:

_____

_____

Correct words:

_____

_____

Spelling Task 3

Read the following passage and identify and correct the spelling errors.

Peopul tend to base their opinnions of others upon their first, visual impresion. Therefore it is important to portray a proffesional appearance that reflects a posative image, as it will affect how other people purceive your abilitys. Key things to consider about your own image are your personal hygene and grooming habits, as these will show you have pride in yourself and the hairdressing services that you offer. As well as your appearance, daily hygiene measures such as taking showers or baths, using deodorant, having clean hair, clean teeth and fresh breath must also be observed. Remember, you tend to get fairly close to people as you are shampooing, cuting, colouring or perming hair.

Key eliments of your overall appearence include hair, skin care and make-up application, hands and nails, and footwear. Hair should be in a styal that does not fall onto the cleint, when leaning forwards, or have the potenstial of getting tangled in equipment. After all, you are virtully a walking advertisment for the hairdressing industry, so it is important to keep up to date with fashion trends and let your hair and make-up reflect this. Your clients may well look to you for inspuration.

Wherever possible, your footwear should be cleen, comfortable and suitable for periods of sustained stannding. Jewelerry should be kept to a sensible amount, bearing in mind that anything ecessive may catch in the client's hair or scratch their skin.

Incorrect words:

Correct words:

Unit 2: Alphabetizing

Short-answer questions

Specific instructions to students

- In this unit, you will be able to practise your alphabetising skills.
- Read the activity below, then answer accordingly.

Alphabetizing Task 1

Put the following words into alphabetical order.

vent brush	colour
barber's chair	tint
sterilize	trolley
brush	hair gel
tail comb	bob
hair wax	fringe
mousse	conditioner

Answer:

_____

_____

_____

_____

_____

_____

_____

_____

_____

_____

_____

_____

_____

Alphabetizing Task 2

Put the following words into alphabetical order.

shampoo	curling tongs	foils	heat protector
stylist	hair spray	autoclave	cash register
hair straighteners	aerosols	hydraulic chair	appointment book
towels	swatches	diffuser	scissors
permanent colour			

Answer:

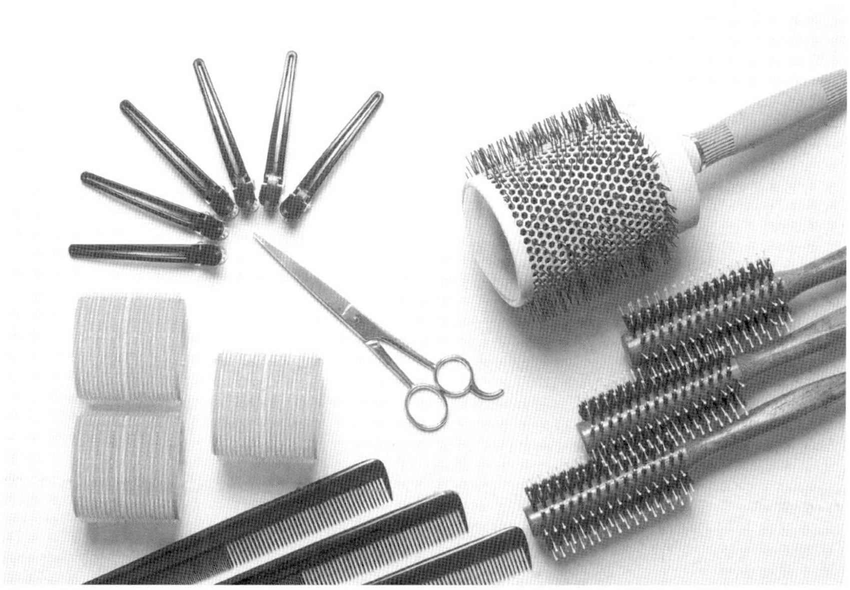

_____

_____

_____

_____

_____

_____

_____

_____

_____

_____

_____

_____

_____

_____

_____

_____

Short-answer questions

Specific instructions to students

- This is an exercise to help you understand what you read.
- Read the following activity, then answer the questions that follow.

Comprehension Task 1

Read the following passage and answer the questions in sentence form.

Jill, the salon owner, had a busy Friday to deal with. She arrived at 7.45 a.m. as she knew the day would be hectic. One stylist had called in sick and there were five brides booked in to have their hair done. As Philip, the junior stylist, arrived, Jill got him into work straight away. One client required a perm, while there were three other clients who needed their hair washed and prepared for cutting. A few clients were booked in for tinting, which was going to keep Philip busy for some time as he needed to prepare the tint, keep an eye on development and wash off. Philip found that all of the clients were patient and he asked one of the work experience students to provide them with tea and coffee as they waited. Elle, the apprentice, started dismantling the clippers, cleaning and oiling them, ready for use. Alisha, another stylist, started cutting a client's hair as another one of the work experience students assisted by sweeping around the chair. The day continued to get busier after that. By the time Jill and the rest of her staff left work at 6.00 p.m., she was looking forward to heading out to meet with friends for drinks.

QUESTION 1

Why did Jill think that the day was going to be a busy one?

Answer:

QUESTION 2

What was the first job that Jill got Philip started on?

Answer:

QUESTION 3

What was the task that was going to keep Philip busy?

Answer:

QUESTION 4

What jobs did the work experience students have to do?

Answer:

_____

_____

QUESTION 5

How long was Jill's work day, from when she arrived at the salon until the time that she left?

Answer:

_____

QUESTION 6

Apart from Jill, the salon owner, and the stylist who is off sick; which members of staff were working on Friday?

Answer:

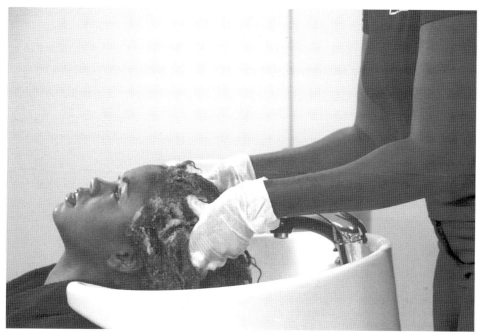

Habia

Comprehension Task 2

Read the following passage and answer the questions in sentence form.

Blake was an apprentice hairdresser and fairly new to his role. He liked to get into work early at 8.30 a.m., and this morning was no exception, even though the first client was not booked in until the salon opened at 9.00 a.m.

His manager, Vanessa, had left him a list of jobs that needed to be done, but he was not sure whether any of the jobs required immediate attention or if they were of equal importance. Vanessa liked him to keep occupied while he was not busy helping out other colleagues in the salon. He checked with his manager to find out which jobs needed doing first, then prioritized the jobs and ticked them off as he carried them out. Vanessa was busy for most of the day interviewing for a new stylist to join the team.

While Blake was carrying out these jobs, he was asked by his colleagues to carry out duties. Helen, the stylist, asked him to shampoo her clients ready for starting her cut and blow-dries. He also swept up hair after each of the five cuts she completed in the morning, before she left for the afternoon, to go to a hospital appointment. Blake managed to take a 15 minute break between helping Helen with her clients and putting towels ready for the laundry collection.

He found that ticking off jobs as he completed them was really helpful, as he had to keep stopping so he could attend to requests from colleagues. Carl, another stylist, wanted him to prepare a trolley for tinting, arrange the foils, and mix the tint ready for application. Carl asked Blake to remove the tint, once it had developed.

Later on in the afternoon, Blake also helped out on reception, as the receptionist had gone home sick at 2.00 p.m. He welcomed clients, found their record cards, and offered them refreshments and magazines. He answered the telephone and took appointments, checking first with Vanessa or Carl that he had taken the correct details and got the right appointment times. It was lucky that he had managed to eat his lunch between 1.00-1.30 p.m.; otherwise it would have been difficult to take a break.

As the last few clients came into the salon, Blake managed a quick break of 10 minutes. When he returned, he tidied the reception area, helped load the towels into the laundry van and unpacked the freshly laundered towels ready for the next day. It had been a long day, but he had enjoyed the variety of jobs that the day had brought. All the staff finished work at the salon at 5.30 p.m. and left to go home.

QUESTION 1

How many clients did Blake shampoo for Helen?

Answer:

QUESTION 2

Who applied the tint to Carl's client?

Answer:

QUESTION 3

Blake started work at 9.00 a.m. and he finished work at 5.30 p.m.; how much time did he take for breaks and lunch?

Answer:

QUESTION 4

What was the manager occupied with for the majority of the day?

Answer:

QUESTION 5

Why did Blake only check with Vanessa or Carl, when making appointments?

Answer:

QUESTION 6

What evidence is there of Blake planning and managing his workload?

Answer:

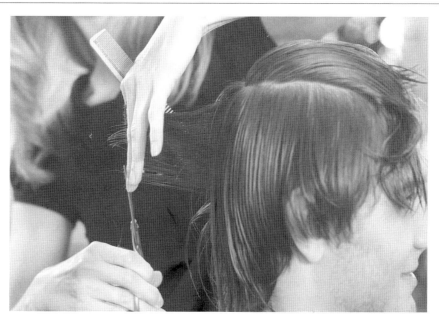

Comprehension Task 3

Read the following passage and answer the questions in sentence form.

Natalia has worked as a stylist in Gino's salon for the last 3 years. She has spotted that the local College is offering a part-time Indian head massage course on Thursday afternoons between 1.00 p.m. to 4.00 p.m. The course lasts for 8 weeks and is due to start in 2 months' time. Natalia sees that this would enable the salon to provide an additional service and bring in new clients. With this in mind, she shows Gino the course details explaining that she will need paid time while she is attending the course and that she would like the salon to pay the £140 course fee.

Gino explains that he will have to consider her request and asks Natalia to attend a structured meeting within the next 28 days to discuss her request and review her training needs in general. During this time, Gino considers if he could fit this service in with what the business offers. He also considers the feasibility of losing staff time; the fees needed for the training course; space availability within the salon to provide this new service, and the additional cost of insurance incurred for offering this service.

Gino arranges a meeting with Natalia to discuss the request and her training needs generally. During this meeting he explains that he does not see Indian head massage becoming part of the services offered by the salon; there just was not enough space to provide the service and it was not in his business plan for the next few years. He went on to explain that the client base was large enough for the two of them and he simply could not afford to lose her one afternoon a week for that length of time. However, during their discussion and review of Natalia's training needs, they both agreed on an action plan for enhancing her skills in advanced colouring techniques, to be carried out through on-the-job refresher training during the next 3 months.

Although Natalia was a little upset at first, she could see that Gino was thinking of the best interest of the business, after all. She could see that Gino had taken her request seriously and had compromised by offering her additional training in advanced colouring techniques, which would update her skills and be beneficial to the business.

QUESTION 1

Why was Natalia interested in attending the Indian head massage course?

Answer:

QUESTION 2

How many hours would Natalia need to be away from the salon to complete the course?

Answer:

QUESTION 3

If Natalia is paid £10 per hour, how much would Gino have to pay her during the time she was away on the course?

Answer:

QUESTION 4

In total, with the course fees, how much would this training request cost Gino?

Answer:

QUESTION 5

How many reasons did Gino give to Natalia why her request was not feasible, at this time, and what were they?

Answer:

QUESTION 6

What compromise did Gino offer Natalia?

Answer:

Unit 4: Homophones

Short-answer questions

Specific instructions to students

- The following questions relate to words that sound the same, but are spelt differently and have different meanings. These words are known as homophones.
- Read the questions carefully, then answer accordingly.

QUESTION 1

The following sentences are about two stylists that have decided to go on holiday together.

a) Check your knowledge of *there*, *their* and *they're* in the following sentences. Only one sentence is correct. Which one is it?

    A They're are too many clients booked in on Friday, for the number of stylists.

    B The manager realized that there holiday will be taken the same time as two others.

    C They're going on their holiday in the early hours of Friday morning.

    D There going to be short staffed on Friday, as their's been too many clients booked in.

Answer

_____

_____

b) Check your knowledge of *where*, *were* and *we're* in the following sentences. Only one sentence is correct. Which one is it?

    A When we get to our destination, we're not sure were we'll go first.

    B We're sure we'll be fine, when we know where we're going.

    C If there's a delay, where sure that we're going to miss our connecting flight.

    D Once we find the hotel, were going to shower and change and go straight out.

Answer

_____

_____

c) Check your knowledge of *too*, *to* and *two* in the following sentences. Only one sentence is correct. Which one is it?

    A The two of us are going to go on holiday to New York too.

    B We want to go too Staten Island too.

    C We're concerned that there'll be two many people on the Metro in New York.

    D To get too Staten Island, the two of us will need to catch the ferry.

Answer

_____

_____

d) Check your knowledge of *buy*, *by* and *bye* in the following sentences. Only one sentence is correct. Which one is it?

    A We'll each have to bye a ticket to get to Staten Island by ferry.

    B By the way, we'll have to make sure that we buy plenty of souvenirs to take home.

    C Buy the time we get home, it will be a struggle to say bye to each other.

    D By all accounts, we'll have to bye some waterproofs for the ferry journey.

Answer

_____

_____

e) Check your knowledge of *pause, paws* and *pours* in the following sentences. Only one sentence is correct. Which one is it?

 A If it paws down with rain, we'll go to Central Park Zoo.

 B If there's a pause in the rain, we'll go and see the polar bears.

 C It doesn't matter if their pours get wet, as they'll be swimming in their pool anyway.

 D Once it starts raining, though, it just paws and paws.

Answer

_____

_____

f) Check your knowledge of *heal, he'll* and *heel* in the following sentences. Only one sentence is correct. Which one is it?

 A While running in the rain, I slipped and fell on my knee and broke the heal of my shoe.

 B My knee is really sore and bruised, so it will take a couple of days to heel.

 C I'm so glad that Andrew is with me, as he'll have to lend me a bit of support.

 D I couldn't find a cobbler, so I'll have to wait to get my heal fixed when I get home.

Answer

_____

_____

QUESTION 2

Check your knowledge of *there, their* and *they're* in the following sentences. Read each sentence and write the correct word in the space provided, from the words provided below:

there   **their**   **they're**

a) The manager chose the shade of towels to complement the colour scheme of _____ salon.

b) _____ was just enough seating in the reception area.

c) I wonder if I could fit another chair in reception, over _____?

d) I've asked the receptionist to welcome the clients and to hang up _____ coats for them.

e) It's nearly 11.00 a.m. and _____ going to be here in a minute.

f) There's a new colour range in stock; I've heard that _____ really good?

g) I believe that the wholesalers have got all of _____ new colour shades in stock.

h) I'll have to go to the wholesalers again, I was only _____ last week.

i) I must leave work on time to get to the wholesalers before _____ closed.

QUESTION 3

Check your knowledge of *where, were* and *we're* in the following sentences. Read each sentence and write the correct word in the space provided, from the words provided below:

where   **were**   **we're**

a) We always make sure that the client is sitting _____ they feel comfortable, ready for their styling service.

b) _____ always making sure that all hairdressing tools are clean and sterilized before use.

c) If the tools aren't sterilized, _____ not prepared to use them due to the risk of cross-infection.

d) When setting out equipment, we always have everything laid out _____ it is in easy reach of the stylist.

e) When cutting hair, _____ always checking that each section is level and contoured to level up with each other.

f) We make sure that any colour work is always carried out _____ there is good light.

g) We make sure that the client has plenty of time to choose from the colour swatches and tend to leave them in view _____ they can refer to them during the service.

h) We always make sure that the client's clothes are hair-free before leaving the salon; there's nothing worse than if the client _____ to have cut hairs in their clothes.

i) If we _____ not to offer any aftercare advice, as part of the hairstyling service, we would be providing a disservice to the client.

j) _____ always happy when a client books in for another hair service, as it shows that they _____ satisfied with the service they received.

QUESTION 4

The following chart relates to words that sound the same, but are spelt differently and have different meanings (homophones). Complete the chart, where applicable, providing clues for the word's meaning and/or a short sentence to put the word in the correct context.

Words	Clues for meaning	Short sentence
Hear	To listen to.	
Here	In this spot.	
Weak		I felt so weak this morning, I could hardly move.
Week	A period of 7 consecutive days.	
Piece		I'll only have a small piece of chocolate cake, thank you.
Peace	Freedom from strife, arguments or war.	
Cue		During the play, he spotted his cue to speak.
Queue	To form a line while waiting.	
Allowed		
Aloud		You're not meant to speak aloud in a library.
Knew	The past tense of 'know'.	
New		

Stationery	Writing materials such as pens, pencils, paper and envelopes.	
Stationary		Locking the castors on a stool makes it stationary.
Whole	The complete sum, amount or quantity of anything.	
Hole		I must have lost my money through the hole in my pocket.
Draught	A current of air, usually of a different temperature, entering an enclosed space.	
Draft	A first sketch, or version, of writing, which could be subject to revision.	
Draw		
Drawer	A lidless container that slides in and out of a chest or table.	

QUESTION 5

Which of these pairs of words are NOT homophones?

A hear/here

B write/right

C stop/cease

D new/knew

Answer

_____

Unit 5: Writing Letters and Emails

Short-answer questions

Specific instructions to students

- The following questions relate to writing letters and emails.
- Read the questions carefully, then answer accordingly.

QUESTION 1

Which type of letter is likely to be informal in style?

A Making an appointment to see the bank manager

B Confirming an interview date

C Email to a friend

D Making a complaint

Answer

QUESTION 2

As well as thinking about the recipient of your letter or email, what else do you need to think about when writing a letter or email?

A The content

B The style

C The layout

D All of the above

Answer

QUESTION 3

True or false? When writing an email, you need to select the email address of the person you want to receive it before selecting the 'send' button.

Answer

QUESTION 4

How would you describe the 'content' of a letter or email?

A The formality with which you are writing

B The ideas and information you are writing

C The amount of text you are writing

Answer

QUESTION 5

When sending an email, if you want other people to receive it but do not want to share their email addresses, which box would you select?

A 'Forward'

B 'Cc'

C 'Bcc'

D 'Send/Receive'

Answer

QUESTION 6

Parts a) to h) relate to this letter of complaint. Please read it carefully and refer to it to answer the questions.

Hair by Bethany Lewis
37 North Street
Millwharf
Ipswich
PE48 7ER
9 April 2012

The Manager
Total Salon Equipment for 21st Century
Fenchurch Street
Leeds
LS17 3QQ

Dear Sir or Madam

Your office contacted me on 15 March regarding the urgent repairs that were required to my 'Universal' accelerator, as the model TWH365 had been identified as representing a fire hazard. Your company service engineer carried out the neccessary repairs on 29 March.

Within a day I noticed that the thermostat was not working correctly, as the heating element overheated and very nearly burned a client. I have had to offer this particular client a complimentary service, as way of compensation for this distressing experience. I have also had to reschedule appointments to allow extra time for development of products, as I cannot run the risk of using this piece of equipment. This has had a knock-on effect of not being able to schedule in as many clients as usual for chemical processes, so I have had to turn away clients, losing the potential earnings of £250.

I rely heavily on the use of this accelerator and the loss of it has caused me great inconvenience and loss of earnings. As none of this is my fault, I am appealing to you to replace my accelerator and to reimburse me for the loss of earnings which I have incurred and for the complimentary service that I had to offer as goodwill to my distressed client.

I hope to hear from you in the near future.

Yours sincerely

Bethany Lewis

---

a) 6. What is wrong with the closing phrase at the end of the letter?

Answer

_____

b) What does the word 'inconvenience' mean, in Line 24?

Answer

_____

c) Which paragraph of the letter outlines the reason for the complaint?

Answer

_____

d) Line 7 contains a spelling error. What is the word and how should it be spelt?

Answer

_____

e) Which word or phrase, used in the letter, means 'to pay me back'?

Answer

_____

f) What is the main complaint in this letter?

Answer

_____

g) How would you describe the style of writing used by Bethany in her letter?

Answer

_____

h) The paragraph of Bethany's letter in which she uses her most persuasive language is?

Answer

_____

QUESTION 7

The following exercises contain a mixture of sentences that have either already been shortened, using apostrophes, or require shortening. Read them carefully, and then reword the sentence accordingly.

a) The stylists are happy, as they've completed their clients and are running ahead of schedule.

Answer

_____

_____

b) They've just spotted that they'll have to order more foils before next week, otherwise they will run out.

Answer

_____

_____

c) I'd love to own my own salon, but I'll have to get more experience before I consider doing so.

Answer

_____

_____

d) They should not be too busy tomorrow, as they have enough staff in the salon to cover all of the appointments.

Answer

_____

_____

_____

e) It is only 10.30 a.m. and I cannot believe how hungry I am!

Answer

_____

f) He won't believe that I missed the last bus home.

Answer

_____

g) She doesn't like to be absent from work as it puts too much pressure on the others.

Answer

_____

_____

QUESTION 8

If you are applying for a job, what do you not need to include?

A What qualifications and experience you have

B Your plans for the future

C How long it will take to commute

D Why you want to work for the company

Answer

_____

QUESTION 9

Rhia has written in response to the advertisement that she spotted in her local newspaper, shown below.

Stylist required for local hair salon.

Must have 2 years' experience.

Please send your CV and covering letter, to:

Jenny Clucas

Red34 at Ledbury

Harley Drive

Ledbury

She has asked you to look over her covering letter to see if she has included all the relevant points, before she posts it. She has also asked if you can help her write it again, if necessary.

Hi there

I want the job you've put in the local news paper this week. I've been in hair for 2 years and I can get people to vouch for me, if you want. Here's a list of my qualifications and where I've worked before, in with this letter.

You can call me on 07562 725094

Rhia

Help Rhia by rewriting the short covering letter to accompany her CV including the correct structure, content and layout for a formal cover letter.

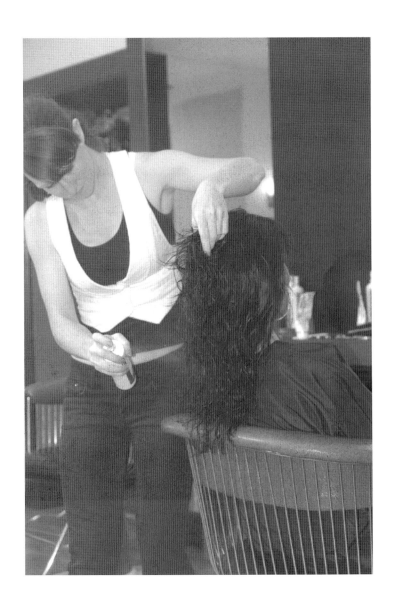

Short-answer questions

Specific instructions to students

- The following questions will help you understand format, style and interpret data.
- Read the following questions, then answer accordingly.

The following questions relate to a Unisex Salon and Nail Bar called 'Top to Toe'. It is set in a busy town location where clients can enjoy a full range of hairdressing, barbering and nail services.

QUESTION 1

Top to Toe has included this diagram in their staff handbook, to show the staff structure. The next few questions are related to this diagram.

a) What is this type of diagram called?

Answer

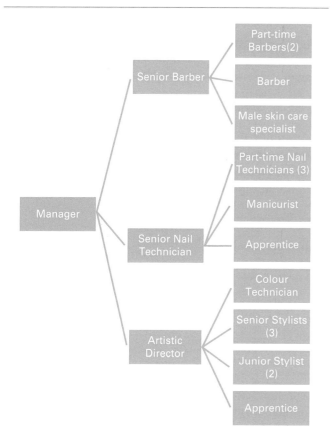

b) How many members of staff is the Artistic Director responsible for?

Answer

c) How many members of staff report directly to the manager?

Answer

d) How many members of staff, including the manager, work at Top to Toe?

Answer

QUESTION 2

The next few questions relate to the holiday entitlements and attendance bonus scheme, provided below, as they appear in the staff handbook at Top to Toe.

Number of years in service	Annual holiday entitlement	❖ Additional holiday for 100% attendance
Less than 1 year	10 days (pro rata)	N/A
1 – 3 years	15 days	0.5 day
4 – 6 years	20 days	1 day
7 – 9 years	25 days	1.5 days
Over 10 years	30 days	2 days

❖ *This additional holiday bonus is only applied in the year following a 100% attendance record*

a) How have the details of the holiday entitlement been presented?

Answer

b) What is the maximum annual holiday entitlement at Top to Toe, without taking any available additional holiday bonus into account?

Answer

c) If a member of staff has worked at Top to Toe for 8 years, how many days holiday are they entitled to?

Answer

_____

d) True or false? The holiday entitlements table provided contains 3 rows and 5 columns.

Answer

_____

e) How much additional time off would a member of staff receive if they had a 100% attendance record in the previous year and had worked for Top to Toe for 11 years?

Answer

_____

f) If a member of staff had a total holiday entitlement of 20 days and 1 day attendance bonus, how long would they have worked at Top to Toe?

Answer

_____

g) What would the total holiday entitlement, including attendance bonus, for a member of staff who had 100% attendance record in their previous year and had worked at Top to Toe for 8 years?

Answer

_____

QUESTION 3

With reference to Top to Toe, the Unisex Salon and Nail Bar, where clients can enjoy a full range of hairdressing, barbering and nail services.

The next few questions relate to the staff handbook that all new members of staff at Top to Toe receive upon starting their employment.

a) The staff handbook is designed to do which of the following?

   A Persuade

   B Advise

   C Instruct

   D Convince

Answer

_____

b) The first page of the staff handbook contains a welcome message from the manager. How would this message be most likely to be presented?

   A In memo format

   B In charts and graphs

   C In paragraphs

   D In bullet points

Answer

_____

c) The staff handbook contains information about actions to take in the case of emergencies, such as discovering a fire in the workplace. This information would be best presented in which of the following forms?

   A Flow chart

   B Pie chart

   C Table

   D Line graph

Answer

_____

d) Assuming that all new employees receive basic training on how to tackle small fires in the workplace, how would it be best to illustrate the use of firefighting equipment in the staff handbook?

   A Using signs

   B Using diagrams

   C Using bar charts

   D Using tables

Answer

_____

e) The staff handbook also includes a Sales Report of retail products over the previous year. The sales achieved in each quarter are displayed in the diagram below. The next few questions relate to this Sales Report.

Top to Toe–Quarterly Sales Report

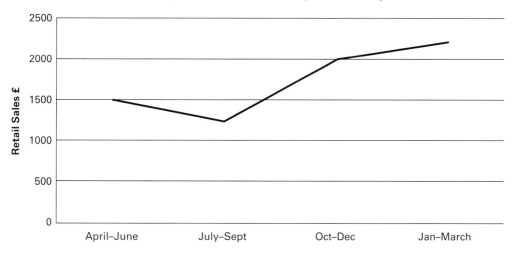

f) How has the information been presented in the Sales Report diagram?

Answer

_____

g) In the Sales Report, during which quarter did Top to Toe have its highest sales?

Answer

_____

h) According to the Sales Report, which quarter did Top to Toe have its biggest sales increase?

Answer

_____

QUESTION 2

The next few questions relate to a local hairdressing salon. The salon has had three pupils, aged 14 and 15, that have attended for work experience, as part of an arrangement with the local High School. They have worked really well over the last 3 months and have fitted into the team of seven stylists extremely well. As a reward and a team-bonding exercise, the manager decides to close the salon on a Wednesday afternoon and take the team out to a 'Handmade Chocolate Making' workshop. She gains parental permission, via the High School, to include the three pupils in the outing.

This table shows the course prices to the Chocolate Making Workshop.

	1 March – 21 March 29 Sept – 13 Nov £	22 March – 12 July 21 Aug – 28 Sept £	13 July – 20 Aug £
Adult	15	21	24
Child (10–15)	7	12	14

a) How much will it cost the manager to take the work experience pupils, the whole team and herself, to the workshop on 15 March?

Answer

_____

b) The Chocolate Making Workshop also operates a retail outlet that sells handmade chocolates to the public. It opens 4 days a week. This table shows the days and the expected number of people to visit each day. The Workshop estimates that usually on a Wednesday, 40% of the customers buy Truffle selection packs. How many Truffle selection packs must they make sure to stock?

Monday	Wednesday	Friday	Saturday
150	90	225	250

Answer

_____

c) The Chocolate Making Workshop records the number of customers that visit the retail outlet on a Saturday. The chart shows the results.

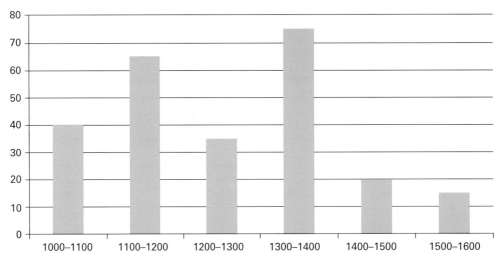

Number of customers visiting the retail outlet per hour

During which 3-hour period did the greatest number of customers visit the retail outlet?

Answer

QUESTION 5

If information is to be organized in terms of a sequence of events, then what order should it be presented in?

Answer

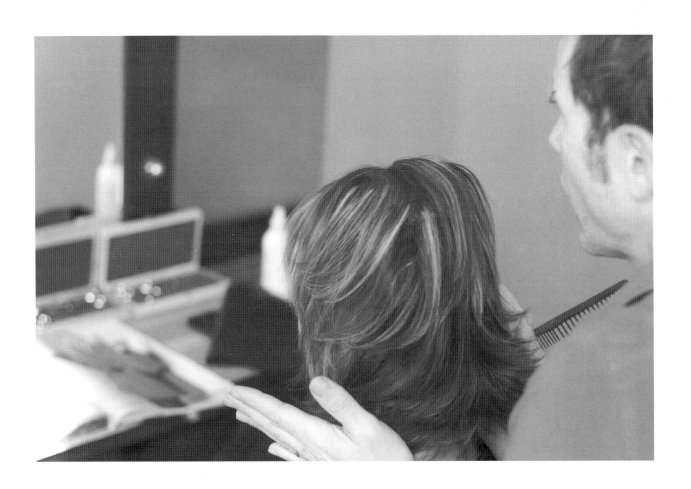

Unit 7: Grammar and Punctuation

Short-answer questions

Specific instructions to students

- The following questions will help you practise your grammar and punctuation.
- Read the following questions, then answer accordingly.

QUESTION 1

Which linking word or phrase could you use instead of 'whereas'?

Answer

QUESTION 2

What does the linking word 'alternatively' mean?

Answer

QUESTION 3

What punctuation is missing from the following sentence?

> A full range of services including cuts colours perms special occasion styles and even Indian head massage are available from the hairdressing salon.

Answer

QUESTION 4

What is wrong with the following text? Correct the following sentence.

> Last Saturday the salon was extremely busy; lanie was run off her feet with all the clients that had been booked in. She was pleased that she had remembered to ask fiona to come in to help. She had felt a bit guilty as she had had to ask fiona to travel in from manchester, where she had been on a hen night the night before.

Answer

QUESTION 5

What is wrong with the following text?

> Why not visit our new hairdressing salon set in the heart of bustling Balham? Youre sure to receive a warm welcome, whether you want a cut, colour, perm, special occasion 'do' or total restyle. The choice is yours! To find out more, call Justine on 01435 778367.

Answer

QUESTION 6

Can you identify the mistake in this job application letter?

> Dear Madam
>
> I wish to apply for the vacancy of junior stylist at your salon, as advertised in this week's Gloucester Globe.
>
> I have just completed my Level 2 NVQ Diploma in Hairdressing coarse at Dinsdale Park College and am now looking for work in the Gloucester area.
>
> I enclose a copy of my CV and look forward to hearing from you.
>
> Yours faithfully
>
>
> Andrew Plessington

Answer

QUESTION 7

a) Add the missing full stops and capital letters to this advert for a barbershop and gents skin care.

b) Can you identify the mistake in this advert?

> **The Male Retreat, Parkgate**
>
> The Male Retreat is a traditional, quality barbershop with olde worlde charm, yet with up to the minute male skin care treatments if you want to experience a full range of male grooming services, with space set aside to unwind and enjoy the peace and quite of professional skin care services The Male Retreat is the place for you please ring 0151 629 4027 to find out more and all about our special offers

Answer

QUESTION 8

Add commas to the following text to make the sense clearer.

> Using a washing machine as we know is a very simple task. Most of us have a washing machine at home yet launderettes are still popular in many locations throughout the UK. Many years ago during Victorian times doing the washing was extremely hard work and took virtually all day. In comparison to those days doing the washing is a piece of cake! Just imagine how long it would have taken in Victorian times to do the laundry that a typical hair salon generates each day nowadays!

Answer

MATHEMATICS

It is important to show your workings out to indicate how you calculated your answer. Use this workbook to practice the questions and record your answers. Use extra paper if necessary to record your workings out.

Unit 8: General Mathematics

Short-answer questions

Specific instructions to students

- This unit will help you to improve your general mathematical skills.
- Read the following questions and answer all of them in the spaces provided.
- You may not use a calculator.
- You need to show all working.

QUESTION 1

What unit of measurement would you use to measure:

a) The length of hair extensions?

Answer:

_____

b) The temperature of an autoclave sterilizer?

Answer:

_____

c) The amount of hair conditioner?

Answer:

_____

d) The weight of a barber's chair?

Answer:

_____

e) The voltage of a hair dryer?

Answer:

_____

f) The length of a tail comb?

Answer:

_____

g) The cost of a blow-dry?

Answer:

_____

QUESTION 2

Write an example of the following and give an instance where it may be used in a hair salon:

a) Percentages

Answer:

_____

b) Decimals

Answer:

_____

c) Fractions

Answer:

_____

d) Mixed numbers

Answer:

_____

e) Ratios

Answer:

_____

f) Angles

Answer:

_____

QUESTION 3
Convert the following units:

a) 12 kg to grams

Answer:

_____

b) 4 tonnes to kilograms

Answer:

_____

c) 120 cm to metres

Answer:

_____

d) 1140 ml to litres

Answer:

_____

e) 1650 g to kilograms

Answer:

_____

f) 1880 kg to tonnes

Answer:

_____

g) 13 m to centimetres

Answer:

_____

h) 4.5 litres to millilitres

Answer:

_____

QUESTION 4
Write the following in descending order:

0.4   0.04   4.1   40.0   400.00   4.0

Answer:

_____

QUESTION 5
Write the decimal number that is between the following:

a) 0.2 and 0.4

Answer:

_____

b) 1.8 and 1.9

Answer:

_____

c) 12.4 and 12.5

Answer:

_____

d) 28.3 and 28.4

Answer:

_____

e) 101.5 and 101.7

Answer:

_____

QUESTION 6
Round off the following numbers to two decimal places:

a) 12.346

Answer:

_____

b) 2.251

Answer:

c) 123.897

Answer:

d) 688.882

Answer:

e) 1209.741

Answer:

QUESTION 7

Calculate the following to the nearest whole number:

a) $1288 \times 19 =$

Answer:

b) $201 \times 20 =$

Answer:

c) $497 \times 12.2 =$

Answer:

d) $1008 \times 10.3 =$

Answer:

e) $399 \times 22 =$

Answer:

f) $201 - 19 =$

Answer:

g) $502 - 61 =$

Answer:

h) $1003 - 49 =$

Answer:

i) $10\ 001 - 199 =$

Answer:

j) $99.99 - 39.8 =$

Answer:

QUESTION 8

What do the following add up to?

a) £4, £4.99 and £144.95

Answer:

b) 8.75, 6.9 and 12.55

Answer:

c) 65 ml, 18 ml and 209 ml

Answer:

d) 21.3 g, 119 g and 884.65 g

Answer:

QUESTION 9

Subtract the following:

a) 2338 from 7117

Answer:

b) 1786 from 3112

Answer:

_____

c) 5979 from 8014

Answer:

_____

d) 11 989 from 26 221

Answer:

_____

e) 108 767 from 231 111

Answer:

_____

QUESTION 10

Use division to solve the following:

a) $2177 \div 7 =$

Answer:

_____

b) $4484 \div 4 =$

Answer:

_____

c) $63.9 \div 0.3 =$

Answer:

_____

d) $121.63 \div 1.2 =$

Answer:

_____

e) $466.88 \div 0.8 =$

Answer:

_____

The following information will help you answer Question 11.

Using the acronym BODMAS, solve the Brackets first, then Of, then Division, Multiplication, then Addition and lastly Subtraction.

EXAMPLE :

Solve $(4 \times 7) \times 2 + 6 - 4$.

STEP 1

Solve the Brackets first: $(4 \times 7) = 28$

STEP 2

No Division so next solve Multiplication: $28 \times 2 = 56$

STEP 3

Addition is next: $56 + 6 = 62$

STEP 4

Subtraction is the last process: $62 - 4 = 58$

FINAL ANSWER

58

_____

QUESTION 11

Using the acronym BODMAS, solve:

a) $(6 \times 9) \times 5 + 7 - 2 =$

Answer:

_____

b) $(9 \times 8) \times 4 + 6 - 1 =$

Answer:

_____

c) $3 \times (5 \times 7) + 11 - 8 =$

Answer:

_____

d) $5 \times (8 \times 3) + 9 - 6 =$

Answer:

_____

e) $7 + 6 \times 3 + (9 \times 6) - 9 =$

Answer:

_____

f) $6 + 9 \times 4 + (6 \times 7) - 21 =$

Answer:

_____

Unit 9: Basic Operations

Section A: Addition

Short-answer questions

Specific instructions to students

- This section will help you to improve your addition skills for basic operations.
- Read the questions below and answer all of them in the spaces provided.
- You may not use a calculator.
- You need to show all working.

QUESTION 1

The salon owner purchases items for the salon which includes: a styling chair for £169, barbering scissors for £25 and a salon backwash basin to fit into an existing unit, for £119. What would be the total cost?

Answer:

QUESTION 2

A client had a wash, cut and blow-dry at £37; another client had a full-head tint costing £60; another had a half-head of foils costing £67. What is the total cost?

Answer:

QUESTION 3

A hair salon wholesaler stocks 127 gowns, 268 jars of hair mousse and 323 various pairs of disposable gloves. How many items are in stock, in total?

Answer:

QUESTION 4

A hairdresser completes cuts at the following prices: a wash, restyle and blow-dry for £40, a wash, cut and blow-dry for £37, a gentleman's cut for £12.50, a children's cut for under 14 years for £15 and a children's cut for under 10 years for £9. How much is the total cost for the cuts?

Answer:

QUESTION 5

A hairdresser uses the following amounts of hair gel in 1 month: 355 ml in week 1, 429 ml in week 2, 869 ml in week 3 and 662 ml in week 4.

a) How many millilitres have been used?

Answer:

b) How many litres have been used?

Answer:

QUESTION 6

An apprentice hairdresser buys a hair care water-mist trigger spray bottle for £3.99, a black cutting cape for £6.25, a hair scissors pouch holster for £22 and a ceramic hair straightener for £36.99. How much has been spent?

Answer:

QUESTION 7

A salon stocks a pack of 300 pre-cut and folded hair foils for £14.35, 50 salon human-hair black extension clips for £11.75 and 30 ml of salon hair treatment for £17.35. What is the total cost of the items?

Answer:

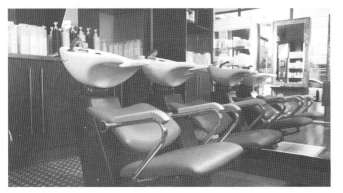

QUESTION 8

A salon owner buys the following fixtures and fittings for the salon: a one position wall styling unit for £512.40, a hydraulic styling chair for £299 and a stand alone backwash unit for £474. How much has been spent?

Answer:

QUESTION 9

A mobile hairdresser travels 3 miles, 7.5 miles, 3 miles and then 8.5 miles, to provide hairdressing services to four different clients, and then travels 10 miles back home. How far has been travelled?

Answer:

QUESTION 10

Three separate hairdressing services cost £37, £88 and £67. How much does the total come to?

Answer:

Section B: Subtraction

Short-answer questions

Specific instructions to students

- This section will help you to improve your subtraction skills for basic operations.
- Read the following questions and answer all of them in the spaces provided.
- You may not use a calculator.
- You need to show all working.

QUESTION 1

A client comes to a salon with hair that is 52 cm in length. The hairdresser cuts off 22 cm but the client is not satisfied and wants shorter hair. If a further 7 cm is cut off, what length remains?

Answer:

QUESTION 2

If one hairdresser travels 36 miles to and from work and another hairdresser travels 19 miles, how much further has the first hairdresser travelled than the second?

Answer:

QUESTION 3

Apprentice A completes various hair services totalling £243. Apprentice B also completes a range of hair services and charges £147. How much more has Apprentice A generated as income?

Answer:

QUESTION 4

A hairdresser uses 39 hair clips from a box that contains 163 hair clips. How many are left?

Answer:

QUESTION 5

A perm, cut and blow-dry costs £67.50. The manager takes off a discount of £15. How much does the customer need to pay?

Answer:

QUESTION 6

Over the course of a year, an apprentice uses 316 hair extensions from a box containing 500 hair extensions. How many are left in the box?

Answer:

QUESTION 7

A salon uses the following amounts of hair conditioner for three cuts: clients with different length and condition of hair; Client A - 55ml; Client B - 38ml and Client C - 69ml. How much conditioner is left from a bottle that contained 250ml of conditioner to begin with?

Answer:

QUESTION 8

A salon manager records 74 cuts in 1 week. If there were a total of 93 cuts booked, how many clients did not turn up or cancelled?

Answer:

QUESTION 9

The overall takings for a salon, for a year, were £171 113. The cost of staff wages came to £84 239. How much was left?

Answer:

QUESTION 10

A hairdresser uses the following amounts of the same tint on three separate clients: 80 ml, 60 ml and 50 ml. If there were 250 ml of tint in a tube to begin with, how much would be left?

Answer:

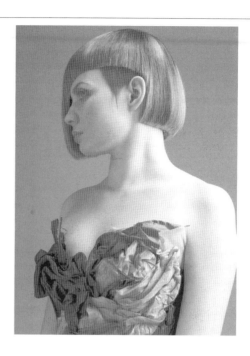

Section C: Multiplication

Short-answer questions

Specific instructions to students

- This section will help you to improve your multiplication skills for basic operations.
- Read the following questions and answer all of them in the spaces provided.
- You may not use a calculator.
- You need to show all working.

QUESTION 1

If a cut, wash and blow-dry costs £37, how much would nine similar services cost?

Answer:

QUESTION 2

If a perm, cut and blow-dry costs £56 how much would three similar services cost?

Answer:

QUESTION 3

An apprentice uses 35 ml of permanent hair colour on one specific style. How much hair colour is used for the same style, if it is completed six times in 1 month?

Answer:

QUESTION 4

A salon purchases six new hydraulic styling chairs at a cost of £298 each. What would the total cost be?

Answer:

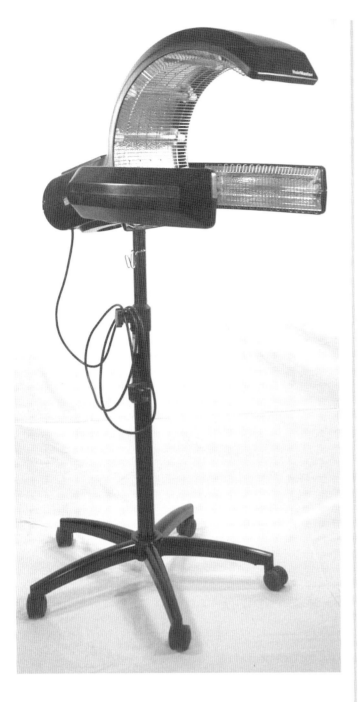

QUESTION 7

A salon uses 9 litres of gel every month. How much gel is used over 18 months?

Answer:

QUESTION 8

If a salon uses 27 pairs of disposable gloves per week, how many would be used over a month (4 weeks)?

Answer:

QUESTION 9

If a hairdresser uses three towels each hour, how many would be used over an 8-hour day?

Answer:

QUESTION 10

If a client who lives in the next city travels 30 miles per hour for 1 hour and 30 minutes to attend a salon, how far have they travelled in total?

Answer:

QUESTION 5

A salon purchases three new backwash chairs at a cost of £358 each. How much would the total cost be?

Answer:

QUESTION 6

A hairdresser charges £62 for a regrowth plus colour-balance-on-ends treatment. How much is charged for eight of the same treatments?

Answer:

Section D: Division

Short-answer questions

Specific instructions to students

- This section will help you to improve your division skills for basic operations.
- Read the following questions and answer all of them in the spaces provided.
- You may not use a calculator.
- You need to show all working.

QUESTION 1

A salon has 24 customers booked in on a Friday morning. If there are four chairs and four hairdressers working, how many customers will each hairdresser attend?

Answer:

QUESTION 2

If a hairdresser earns £518 (before tax) for working a 5-day week, how much would they earn per day?

Answer:

QUESTION 3

A salon owner buys 210 bottles of anti-dandruff shampoo in bulk. Each box contains 30 bottles. How many boxes are there?

Answer:

QUESTION 4

A hairdresser has 720 clients in 6 months. On average, how many clients are there per month?

Answer:

QUESTION 5

An apprentice puts highlights in four clients' hair. The total cost comes to £260. How much is this per client, on average?

Answer:

QUESTION 6

One month's takings for a salon are £13 925. How much are the takings, on average, per week (given that there are 4 weeks in each month)?

Answer:

QUESTION 7

At an annual stocktake, a store person at a hairdressing wholesaler warehouse counts 648 scissors. If they are packed so that there are six in each box, how many boxes would there be?

Answer:

QUESTION 8

Four hundred and eight gowns are ordered for a salon. If there are four in each packet, how many packets are there?

Answer:

QUESTION 9

A salon has takings of £6862 over 6 days. How much, on average, does the salon make per day?

Answer:

QUESTION 10

An apprentice uses 144 foils on 12 clients. How many foils is this per client, on average?

Answer:

Section A: Addition

Short-answer questions

Specific instructions to students

- This section will help you to improve your addition skills when working with decimals.
- Read the following questions and answer all of them in the spaces provided.
- You may not use a calculator.
- You need to show all working.

Habia

QUESTION 1

If four new lockable hairdressing trolleys are purchased for £946.88 and a styling chair for £209.75, how much is the total?

Answer:

QUESTION 2

An apprentice hairdresser buys a set of brushes for £39.95, some hair lightener for £24.95, several combs for £44.55 and a set of rollers for £59.45. How much has been spent?

Answer:

QUESTION 3

The length of one hair extension is 25.5 cm and another is 30.5 cm. What is the total length of the two extensions?

Answer:

QUESTION 4

A client purchases a paddle brush for £15.50 and a round brush for £8.50. How much is the total?

Answer:

QUESTION 5

A hairdresser buys the following: a hair styling gel for £8.99, hair clips for £6.50, hair mousse for £12.30 and a tinting apron for £5.90. What is the total?

Answer:

QUESTION 6

If a lorry driver who delivers salon products travels 65.8 miles, 36.5 miles, 22.7 miles and 89.9 miles, how far has the driver travelled to deliver the goods?

Answer:

QUESTION 7

A client asks for a single foil that costs £7.50 and his partner wants three foils costing £22.50. What is the total?

Answer:

QUESTION 8

Two clients ask for three foils costing £22.50 and nine foils costing £67.50 respectively. How much will the total cost be for both clients?

Answer:

QUESTION 9

A hair stylist completes three hairdressing services. The first service is £45.80, the second is £130.65 and the third is £66.45. How much has been charged in total?

Answer:

QUESTION 10

A salon's takings for the first hour after opening are £89.90, £45.50, £55.50, £135.50 and £32.50. What are the total takings for the first hour?

Answer:

Section B: Subtraction

Short-answer questions

Specific instructions to students

- This section will help you to improve your subtraction skills when working with decimals.
- Read the following questions and answer all of them in the spaces provided.
- You may not use a calculator.
- You need to show all working.

QUESTION 1

A salon's takings in the morning are £338.68. The manager pays for lunch for the staff and spends £43.95 on food and drinks. How much is left out of the takings?

Answer:

QUESTION 2

A stylist gets paid £568.50 for a week's work. If they use £243.50 to pay bills, £55.75 is paid for petrol and £76 is spent on entertainment, how much do they have left?

Answer:

QUESTION 3

A hairdresser completes a style that costs £97.50 and then a discount of £25.00 is given. How much is the final cost?

Answer:

QUESTION 4

An apprentice earns £245.60. The apprentice uses £48.85 for petrol and £38.75 for going out. How much is left?

Answer:

QUESTION 5

A client's bill for hairdressing services and retail products comes to £90.50. The client pays with 5 x £20 notes. How much change is given?

Answer:

QUESTION 6

If a client pays £22.50 for products with 2 x £20 notes, how much change is given?

Answer:

QUESTION 7

The members of a bridal party have their hair styled for the wedding day. They have pooled their money together. Their bill comes to £432.50. What change is given if they hand over ten £50 notes?

Answer:

QUESTON 8

A 250 ml tube of hair colour is used on three different hairstyles: 25 ml for the first style, 36 ml on the second and 13 ml on the third. How much is left in the tube?

Answer:

QUESTION 9

A salon has four clients that require different hairdressing services. One client had a full-head tint (£65.50); another client had a full-head of foils (£77.50); another client had a half-head of foils (£67.50); and the fourth client had a perm (£56.00). If the cash till has £490 in it after the clients have paid for their services, how much float was in the till before they paid?

Answer:

QUESTION 10

A hair dresser buys two hair dryers for £38.50 each. If 2 × £50 notes are used to pay the bill, how much change is given?

Answer:

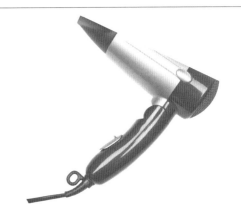

Section C: Multiplication

Short-answer questions

Specific instructions to students

- This section will help you to improve your multiplication skills when working with decimals.
- Read the following questions and answer all of them in the spaces provided.
- You may not use a calculator.
- You need to show all working.

QUESTION 1

If one tint brush costs £9.95, how much will five tint brushes cost?

Answer:

QUESTION 2

If a hairdresser uses six packets of foils on average each week, how many packets are used in 1 year?

Answer:

QUESTION 3

A salon manager replaces six pairs of 6-inch scissors at a cost of £34.50 each. What is the total?

Answer:

QUESTION 4

If a salon purchases six bales of towels that cost £38.65 per bale, how much is the total cost?

Answer:

QUESTION 5

A manager buys 12 capes that cost £19.95 each. What is the total cost?

Answer:

QUESTION 6

If a stylist earns £15.50 per hour and the working week is 45 hours, how much would be earned in a week?

Answer:

QUESTION 7

The manager of a hairdressing franchise buys portable air conditioners for £682.50 per unit for her eight salons. How much has been spent?

Answer:

QUESTION 8

A salon product delivery van drops off 75 1-litre conditioner bottles to a salon at a cost of £19.85 per bottle. How much will the total invoice be?

Answer:

QUESTION 9

A manager purchases five gallery workstations for the salon at a cost of £255 each. How much is the outlay?

Answer:

QUESTION 10

A hairdresser earns £130.65 per day before tax. How much is earned for a 5-day week?

Answer:

Section D: Division

Short-answer questions

Specific instructions to students

- This section will help you to improve your division skills when working with decimals.
- Read the following questions and answer all of them in the spaces provided.
- You may not use a calculator.
- You need to show all working.

QUESTION 1

A hairdresser earns £628.55 for a 6-day working week. How much is earned for each day?

Answer:

QUESTION 2

A manager earns £790.60 for 5 days work. How much is earned per day?

Answer:

QUESTION 3

A salon's takings are £2245.50 over 5 days. How much are the daily takings, on average?

Answer:

QUESTION 4

A stylist completes perms on three clients. The total cost comes to £231.90. How much is this, on average, per client?

Answer:

QUESTION 5

Three clients have full-head foils at a total cost of £246.90. How much is each client charged?

Answer:

QUESTION 6

Four clients have long hair that requires a wash, cut and blow-dry. The total bill comes to £148.80. How much does each client pay?

Answer:

QUESTION 7

Six male clients are charged the same amount to have a haircut. The takings comes to £105.00. How much is each client charged?

Answer:

QUESTION 8

A salon completes five full-head tint applications for five different clients. The total charged for all five applications is £347.50. How much is each client charged?

Answer:

QUESTION 9

Eight clients are charged a total of £464.80 to get highlights using a freehand technique. How much is the cost per client?

Answer:

QUESTION 10

Three clients with short hair have a wash, semi-permanent colour and blow-dry. The total comes to £173.25. How much is each client charged?

Answer:

Unit 11: Fractions

Section A: Addition

Short-answer questions

Specific instructions to students

- This section is designed to help you to improve your addition skills when working with fractions.
- Read the following questions and answer all of them in the spaces provided.
- You may not use a calculator.
- You need to show all working.

QUESTION 1

$\frac{1}{2} + \frac{4}{5} =$

Answer:

QUESTION 2

$2\frac{2}{4} + 1\frac{2}{3} =$

Answer:

QUESTION 3

Two bottles of shampoo are each $\frac{1}{3}$ full. How much shampoo, as a fraction of a bottle, is there in total?

Answer:

QUESTION 4

An apprentice has two clients who want foils. One client wants one-quarter-head foils and the other client wants three-quarter-head foils. Using a fraction, show the total amount of head foils.

Answer:

QUESTION 5

A tint bowl has $\frac{2}{3}$ of a small bottle of red hair colour in it. To make a shade of orange, another $\frac{1}{4}$ of a small bottle of yellow hair colour is added. How much hair colour in total is in the tint bowl, as a fraction?

Answer:

Section B: Subtraction

Short-answer questions

Specific instructions to students

- This section is designed to help you to improve your subtraction skills when working with fractions.
- Read the following questions and answer all of them in the spaces provided.
- You may not use a calculator.
- You need to show all working.

QUESTION 1

$\frac{2}{3} - \frac{1}{4} =$

Answer:

QUESTION 2

$2\frac{2}{3} - 1\frac{1}{4} =$

Answer:

QUESTION 3

A bottle of hair lightening product is $\frac{2}{3}$ full. If $\frac{1}{3}$ is used on a treatment, how much hair lightening product is left as a fraction of the bottle?

Answer:

QUESTION 4

A hairdresser has $2\frac{1}{2}$ containers of hair gel. If $1\frac{1}{3}$ is used on two different clients, how much hair gel is left, as a fraction of a container?

Answer:

QUESTION 5

An apprentice has $2\frac{3}{4}$ bottles of hydrogen peroxide in a salon. If $1\frac{1}{2}$ bottles are used over 2 weeks, how much is left in total as a fraction?

Answer:

Section C: Multiplication

Short-answer questions

Specific instructions to students

- This section is designed to help you to improve your multiplication skills when working with fractions.
- Read the following questions and answer all of them in the spaces provided.
- You may not use a calculator.
- You need to show all working.

QUESTION 1

$\frac{2}{4} \times \frac{2}{3} =$

Answer:

QUESTION 2

$2\frac{2}{3} \times 1\frac{1}{2} =$

Answer:

QUESTION 3

An apprentice uses two bottles of conditioner that are each $\frac{2}{3}$ full. What is the total amount of conditioner used as a fraction?

Answer:

QUESTION 4

A hairdresser uses three bottles of hydrogen peroxide that are $\frac{3}{4}$ full over a week. How much is used as a fraction?

Answer:

QUESTION 5

A hairdresser uses four small bottles of hair styling lotion that are each $\frac{1}{3}$ full at the end of the week. How much is used as a fraction?

Answer:

Section D: Division

Short-answer questions

Specific instructions to students

- This section has been designed to help you to improve your division skills when working with fractions.
- Read the following questions and answer all of them in the spaces provided.
- You may not use a calculator.
- You need to show all working.

QUESTION 1

$\frac{2}{3} \div \frac{1}{4} =$

Answer:

QUESTION 2

$2\frac{3}{4} \div 1\frac{1}{3} =$

Answer:

QUESTION 3

An apprentice needs to distribute the contents of three hydrogen peroxide bottles evenly into four empty bottles in order to dilute it. As a fraction, how much will be in each of the four bottles?

Answer:

QUESTION 4

A hairdresser has three empty bottles and two full bottles of hair colour. He wants to transfer and then mix the colour. He needs to transfer the hair colour evenly to each empty bottle. As a fraction, how much colour will be evenly transferred to each of the three empty bottles?

Answer:

QUESTION 5

A hairdresser wants to apply a colour and needs it diluted. Two bottles of colour are poured into six empty bottles. As a fraction, how much will be poured into each of the six empty bottles from the two full colour bottles?

Answer:

Short-answer questions

Specific instructions to students

- In this unit, you will be able to practise and improve your skills in working out percentages and ratios.
- Read the following questions and answer all of them in the spaces provided.
- You may not use a calculator.
- You need to show all working.

Section A: Percentages

> 10% rule: Move the decimal one place to the left to get 10%.

EXAMPLE

10% of £45.00 would be £4.50

QUESTION 1

A bill for restyles and foils for two bridesmaids comes to £220.00. The customer has a voucher for a 10% discount.

a) What will the discount be?

Answer:

b) What will the bill come to after the 10% is taken off?

Answer:

QUESTION 2

A client has cut, blow-dry and full-head foils costing £175.00. A '10% off' voucher is used to reduce the final cost.

a) How much will the discount be?

Answer:

b) How much is the final bill?

Answer:

QUESTION 3

A salon has an air-conditioning system installed for £2598.50. The salon was given a 10% discount on the purchase.

a) How much will the discount be?

Answer:

b) What is the final cost?

Answer:

QUESTION 4

A manager buys five sets of curling tongs at a wholesale price of £124.80. A 5% discount is given.

a) How much is the discount worth?

Answer:

b) What is the final total? (Hint: Find 10%, halve it, then subtract it from the individual price of each set of curling tongs.)

Answer:

QUESTION 5

An apprentice buys three gowns for £20 each, a hair dryer for £69 and a set of hair rollers for £13.

a) How much is the total?

Answer:

b) How much would a 20% discount be?

Answer:

c) What is the final cost after discount?

Answer:

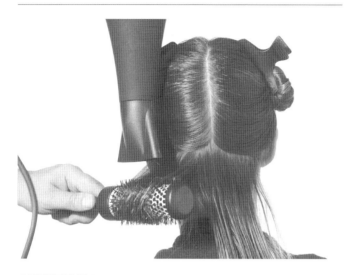

QUESTION 6

The following items are purchased for a salon: one box of disposable gloves costing £18, 12 bottles of sculpting mousse for £109, a professional clipper for £19.99, a hair dryer for £72 and six towels for £49.

a) What is the total?

Answer:

b) How much would be a 10% discount?

Answer:

c) What is the final cost after the discount?

Answer:

QUESTION 7

A salon offers 20% off the price of any salon product purchase over £55. If a client spends £105 in total, how much would the heat protection lotion, normally priced at £36, cost?

Answer:

QUESTION 8

A particular range of hair care products are discounted by 15%. If the recommended retail price is £45.50 for one of these particular products, what will be the discounted price?

Answer:

QUESTION 9

A brand of hair spray costs £16.90 as per the recommended retail price. The salon has a '20% sale' on this item. How much will the hair spray cost during the sale?

Answer:

QUESTION 10

Shampoo and conditioner for damaged hair retails for £29. During a sale, the product is sold at 30% off. What will the selling price be after the discount?

Answer:

20% off

The price of any salon product purchase over £55.00

Section B: Ratios

Short-answer questions

Specific instructions to students

- This section will help you to improve your skills when working with ratios. Remember, ratios are a way to compare the amounts of something.
- Read the following questions and answer all of them in the spaces provided.
- You may not use a calculator.
- You need to show all working.

QUESTION 1

Your manager wants you to mix some disinfectant fluid; they have asked you to make up a litre (1000 ml).
The instructions state to mix disinfectant fluid and water in a ratio of 3:1. How much of each ingredient should you measure?

Answer

QUESTION 2

An exercise plan states that you should go 3 miles, jogging and walking in the ratio of 4:2.

How far should you jog and how far should you walk?

Answer

QUESTION 3

If fruit cordial and water are mixed together at a ratio of 1:8, how much water would you need to result in 360 ml?

Answer

QUESTION 4

During a single day, the salon performs services on 15 female clients and 12 male clients. What is the ratio of female to male clients? Give your answer in its simplest form.

Answer

QUESTION 5

A spa treatment brochure includes 12 pages of complementary, holistic and spa treatments and images, and 8 pages of hair and nail services.

What is the ratio of complementary, holistic and spa treatments to hair and nail services? Give your answer in its simplest form.

Answer

Unit 13: Measurement Conversions

Short-answer questions

Specific instructions to students

- This unit is designed to help you to improve your skills and increase your speed in converting one measurement into another.
- Read the following questions and answer all of them in the spaces provided.
- You may not use a calculator.
- You need to show all working.

QUESTION 1

How many millimetres are there in 1 cm?

Answer:

_____

QUESTION 2

How many centimetres are there in 1 m?

Answer:

_____

QUESTION 3

How many millimetres are there in 1 m?

Answer:

_____

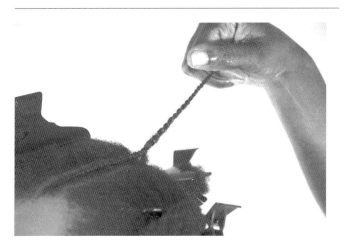

QUESTION 4

If there are two braids in 2 cm, how many braids would be in 10 cm?

Answer:

_____

QUESTION 5

How many millilitres are there in a 1.5 litre bottle of anti-dandruff shampoo?

Answer:

_____

QUESTION 6

How many litres does 3500 ml of hair bleach make?

Answer:

_____

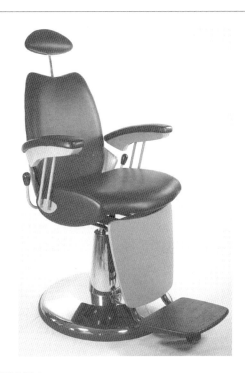

QUESTION 7

A barber's chair weighs a quarter of a tonne. How many kilograms is that?

Answer:

_____

QUESTION 8

A delivery truck weighs 2 tonnes. How many kilograms is that?

Answer:

_____

QUESTION 9

A hair product delivery truck weighs 4750 kg. How many tonnes is that?

Answer:

QUESTION 10

A salon floor measures 4.8 m wide and 12 m long. How far is it around the perimeter of the salon?

Answer:

TIP

From time to time, it may be necessary to be able to convert inches to centimetres, for example, when selecting lengths for hair extensions.

Remember: 1 inch = 2.54 cm (you can round this down to 2.5 cm if you wish)

QUESTION 11

Julie is a first year apprentice who is asked to use hair extensions that are 5 inches. What would this length be in centimetres?

Answer:

QUESTION 12

On Tuesday, Meesha had two clients who wanted hair extensions. One client wanted 8-inch hair extensions and the other wanted 12-inch hair extensions. What lengths are these in centimetres?

Answer:

QUESTION 13

Jenna is going to the end of school prom and she wants 18-inch hair extensions. How long will these be in centimetres?

Answer:

QUESTION 14

Liam was working on a mannequin head block and wanted to add 14-inch human hair extensions. How long would they be in centimetres?

Answer:

QUESTION 15

Paula loved long hair and decided to get 20-inch hair extensions. How long would her hair extensions be in centimetres?

Answer:

QUESTION 16

Ali wanted 25 cm hair extensions. How long would these be in inches? (Hint: divide 25 by 2.5)

Answer:

QUESTION 17

A mannequin head block has hair added at a length of 30 cm. How long is this in inches?

Answer:

QUESTION 18

Kirsty is getting married on Saturday. She wants to have hair extensions that are 50 cm long. How long will the hair extensions be in inches?

Answer:

QUESTION 19

Gabrielle enters a salon and wants a short haircut. The cut is to be 5 cm long. What length is this in inches?

Answer:

QUESTION 20

After washing a client's long hair, Daryle asks that it be cut to a length of approximately 35 cm. How long is this in inches?

Answer:

Unit 14: Time

Short-answer questions

Specific instructions to students

- This unit will help you understand the 24-hour clock and how to calculate how long you need to complete the service.
- Read the following questions and answer all of them in the spaces provided.
- You may not use a calculator.
- You need to show all working.

QUESTION 1

What is 23:17 in 12-hour time?

Answer

QUESTION 2

What is 3.56pm in 24-hour time?

Answer

QUESTION 3

A Hairdressing Apprentice needs to catch the 07:50 train to London to get to the salon where she works. The train arrives in London at 09:06; how long does the journey take?

Answer

QUESTION 4

A salon receptionist needs to catch a train back from London, so that he arrives at his home station as close to 8pm as possible, which of the following trains would be the best (assuming that his journey took approximately 1 hour 30 minutes)?

A) 1545

B) 1956

C) 1735

D) 0538

Answer

QUESTION 5

A customer books an appointment for a full-head of highlights for midday. What time is midday on a 24-hour clock?

Answer

QUESTION 6

What time is midnight on a 24-hour clock?

Answer

QUESTION 7

Complete the client appointment book for Beautiful Cuts salon to include the following appointments for the salon's senior hairdresser.

Lena Brooks would like a cut and blow-dry for the morning.
Julian Crane would like a men's cut after 10 a.m.
Reese Lamb would like a full-head of highlights to start before 11 a.m.

Cut and blow-dry will take 45 minutes
Men's haircut will take 30 minutes.
Full head of highlights will take 60 minutes to apply.

Time	Client	Service
9:00		
9:15		
9:30		
9:45		
10:00		
10:15		
10:30		
10:45		
11:00		
11:15		
11:30		
11:45		
12:00		

Unit 15: Earning Wages

Short-answer questions

Specific instructions to students

- This unit will help you to calculate how much a service is worth and how long you need to complete the service.
- Read the following questions and answer all of them in the spaces provided.
- You may not use a calculator.
- You need to show all working.

QUESTION 1

Sue, the first year apprentice, earns £260.60 net (take home per week). How much does Sue earn per year? (Remember, there are 52 weeks in a year.)

Answer:

QUESTION 2

A hairdresser starts work at 8.00 a.m. and has a break at 10.30 a.m. for 20 minutes. Lunch starts at 12.30 p.m. and finishes at 1.30 p.m. The hairdresser then works through to 4.00 p.m.

a) How long are the breaks in total, in minutes?

Answer:

b) How many hours and minutes have been worked in total, excluding breaks?

Answer:

QUESTION 3

A hairdresser earns £12.50 an hour and works a 38-hour week. How much are his weekly gross earnings (before tax)?

Answer:

QUESTION 4

A hairdresser gets paid £513 net for her week's work. From her earnings she buys new clothes at a cost of £46.90, jewellery worth £49.50, CDs worth £59.97 and a bus ticket which costs £12.60. She also spends £55 on entertainment.

a) What is the total of all money spent?

Answer:

b) How much is left?

Answer:

QUESTION 5

Several clients enter a salon and the hairdresser there takes the following amount of time for each client: 34 minutes, 18 minutes, 7 minutes, 44 minutes and 59 minutes. How much time, in hours and minutes, has been spent on these clients in total?

Answer:

QUESTION 6

A hairdresser has a client who requires permanent hair colouring. This takes the hairdresser $1\frac{1}{2}$ hours to complete. How many hours are left if the hairdresser normally works an 8-hour day?

Answer:

QUESTION 7

A hairdresser wants to create more movement and greater lift in a hairstyle for a client. This takes $1\frac{1}{2}$ hours to complete. A second client requires a regrowth treatment plus colour balance on the ends. This takes $1\frac{1}{4}$ hours.

a) How many hours were spent on the two clients? State your answer as a fraction.

Answer:

_____

b) If the hairdresser works an 8-hour day, how many hours are left? State your answer as a fraction.

Answer:

_____

QUESTION 8

If it takes the hairdresser 1 hour and 45 minutes to complete a perm on a client with long hair, how long (in hours and minutes) will be left in an 8-hour working day?

Answer:

_____

QUESTION 9

A salon manager begins work at 7.00 a.m. and works until 4.00 p.m. She takes a morning break for 20 minutes, a lunch break for 60 minutes and an afternoon break of 20 minutes.

a) How much time has been spent on breaks?

Answer:

_____

b) How much time has been spent working?

Answer:

_____

QUESTION 10

If a salon's daily takings come to £850.50 and the salon manager spent 10 hours at the salon working alone, how much is the rate, on average, of the takings per hour?

Answer:

_____

Unit 16: Squaring Numbers

Section A: Introducing square numbers

Short-answer questions

Specific instructions to students

- This section is designed to help you to improve your skills and increase your speed in squaring numbers.
- Read the following questions and answer all of them in the spaces provided.
- You may not use a calculator.
- You need to show all working.

Any number squared is multiplied by itself.

EXAMPLE

4 squared $= 4^2 = 4 \times 4 = 16$

QUESTION 1

$6^2 =$

Answer:

QUESTION 2

$8^2 =$

Answer:

QUESTION 3

$12^2 =$

Answer:

QUESTION 4

$3^2 =$

Answer:

QUESTION 5

$7^2 =$

Answer:

QUESTION 6

$11^2 =$

Answer:

QUESTION 7

$10^2 =$

Answer:

QUESTION 8

$9^2 =$

Answer:

QUESTION 9

$2^2 =$

Answer:

QUESTION 10

$4^2 =$

Answer:

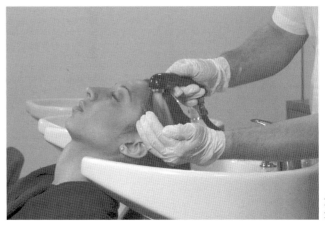

Habia

Section B: Applying square numbers in the trade

Worded practical problems

Specific instructions to students

- This section is designed to help you to improve your skills and increase your speed in calculating volumes of rectangular or square objects. The worded questions make the content relevant to everyday situations.
- Read the following questions and answer all of them in the spaces provided.
- You may not use a calculator.
- You need to show all working.

QUESTION 1

If there are 5 × 5 hair spray cans in a box, how many cans are there in total?

Answer:

_____

QUESTION 2

A box of shampoo arrives at a salon stacked 6 × 6. What is the total number of bottles of shampoo?

Answer:

_____

QUESTION 3

There are 12 × 12 round brushes packed into a box. How many are in the box?

Answer:

_____

QUESTION 4

A warehouse floor has an area that is 15 m × 15 m. How much floor area is this in square metres (m²)?

Answer:

_____

QUESTION 5

A merchandise box contains hair gel tubes that are in rows of 8 × 8. How many tubes of hair gel are there?

Answer:

_____

QUESTION 6

A salon manager unpacks two boxes to put on display. The first box contains 4 × 4 cans of hair spray. The second box contains hair wax that is packed in a 3 × 3 formation. How many stock items are there in total?

Answer:

_____

QUESTION 7

A box of shampoo and conditioner bottles arrive at a salon. If they are packed in a 20 × 20 formation, how many are there?

Answer:

_____

QUESTION 8

A salon stocks the following: 5 × 5 tint bowls, 3 × 3 capes and 7 × 7 vent brushes. How many items of stock are there in total?

Answer:

_____

QUESTION 9

A colour shade chart consists of 5 × 5-inch light strands, 5 × 5-inch medium strands and 5 × 5-inch dark strands. How many individual strands are there in total?

Answer:

_____

QUESTION 10

A colour shade chart consists of the following: 3 × 3 dark pieces; 3 × 3 medium pieces; 3 × 3 medium-dark pieces and 3 × 3 white pieces. How many pieces are there in total?

Answer:

_____

Short-answer questions

Specific instructions to students

- This unit will help you to calculate the details of vouchers.
- Read the following questions and answer all of them in the spaces provided.
- You may not use a calculator.
- You need to show all working.

QUESTION 1

A client has a wash, cut and blow-dry that comes to £50. The client has a voucher for 20% off.

a) How much is taken off for the voucher?

Answer:

_____

b) How much is the final cost?

Answer:

_____

QUESTION 2

A father and his son get their hair washed, cut and blow-dried before returning to work and school respectively after the holidays. The salon charges £45 for the father's cut and £25 for the son's haircut. They also purchase hair gel for £8.50, shampoo for £13.50 and a new vent brush for £12.50. They have a '15% off' voucher that covers both cuts and products.

a) What is the total before taking off the value of the voucher?

Answer:

_____

b) How much is the voucher worth?

Answer:

_____

c) What is the total after the value of the voucher is taken off?

Answer:

_____

QUESTION 3

A client purchases some goods from a salon. They include: two jars of hair gel for £22.95, a paddle brush for £15.95, a fine tail comb for £9.99 and some texturizer for £14.95. The client has a '30% off' voucher on all items.

a) What is the total cost before using the voucher?

Answer:

_____

b) How much is the voucher worth?

Answer:

_____

c) What is the final cost after using the voucher?

Answer:

_____

QUESTION 4

A family of four comes into a salon for haircuts. One person has a full restyle and highlights, which costs £95; another person has a tint costing £50; a child has a haircut costing £15 and another child has short hair that requires a treatment costing £45. The family has a voucher for '25% off'.

a) What is the total before using the voucher?

Answer:

_____

b) How much is the voucher worth?

Answer:

_____

c) What will be the final total after using the voucher?

Answer:

_____

QUESTION 5

A salon manager purchases equipment to update their salon. The manager buys four hydraulic chairs for £968, two lockable hairdressing trolleys for £525, six-dozen bleach-proof towels for £348 and three mannequin head blocks for £65. The manager has a '15% off' voucher on all goods.

a) What is the total before using the voucher?

Answer:

_____

b) How much is the voucher worth?

Answer:

_____

c) How much will the salon manager need to pay after using the voucher?

Answer:

_____

QUESTION 6

A client enters a salon with a '25% off' gift voucher that she received for her birthday. The client decides to have foils so as to have streaks of colour to help give her hair definition. The cost is £155.00.

a) How much will the voucher take off the cost?

Answer:

_____

b) What will the final cost be?

Answer:

_____

QUESTION 7

Three clients in a salon have vouchers for '15% off'. They have services costing £60, £35 and £25 respectively.

a) How much does the voucher reduce the cost for each customer?

Answer:

_____

b) How much is the total for each client after using the voucher?

Answer:

_____

QUESTION 8

A wedding party is booked in for various hair services on the morning of the wedding. The bride's hairstyle costs £110. There are four bridesmaids and each of their styles costs £95. The bridal party has a '15%' gift voucher as a present from some of the guests.

a) What is the cost before the voucher?

Answer:

_____

b) By how much will the voucher reduce the price?

Answer:

_____

c) What is the final cost to the bridal party?

Answer:

_____

Habia

QUESTION 9

A local salon approaches a high school and offers '15% off' vouchers to students wanting to have their hair styled for the forthcoming end of year prom. Eighty-three students decide to take up the offer. The cost of each service before using the voucher is £55.

a) What is the total cost for all 83 students to get their hair styled before using the voucher?

Answer:

_____

b) What is the cost for one service after using the '15% off' voucher?

Answer:

_____

c) How much in total will the '15% off' vouchers take off the price for the whole group of 83 students?

Answer:

_____

d) What will the final takings be for the salon from the group of 83 students?

Answer:

_____

QUESTION 10

The end of year prom is in a week and a salon decides to offer vouchers to any students who want to get their hair cut and blow-dried for the occasion. The vouchers offer a 25% discount, but only if over 100 students take up the offer. One hundred and seven students decide to get their hair cut and blow-dried. The salon charges £45 per cut and blow-dry.

a) What is the total cost for the 107 students before using the '25% off' voucher?

Answer:

_____

b) By how much does the voucher reduce the cost?

Answer:

_____

c) What is the final cost for the whole group of 107 students?

Answer:

_____

Unit 18: Deals

Short-answer questions

Specific instructions to students

- This unit will help you to calculate the details of deals.
- Read the following questions and answer all of them in the spaces provided.
- You may not use a calculator.
- You need to show all working.

QUESTION 1

A salon sells a bottle of shampoo for £14.50 each or two for £26.

a) Which is the better deal and why?

Answer:

_____

b) How much is the price difference per bottle?

Answer:

_____

QUESTION 2

A salon sells mousse for £8.95 per bottle or two for £15.

a) Which is the better buy?

Answer:

_____

b) How much is the difference per bottle?

Answer:

_____

QUESTION 3

A salon has an offer for clients to buy one bottle of conditioner for £12.50 or three bottles of the same product for £40.

a) Which is the better deal?

Answer:

_____
_____

b) How much is the difference?

Answer:

_____

QUESTION 4

A salon offers clients a hair care product for £7.95 or 'buy two, get one free' for £22. Which is the better buy and why?

Answer:

_____
_____
_____

QUESTION 5

A client wants to buy hair spray and a salon has an offer of one can for £11.95 or 'buy one, get one free' for £23. Which is the better deal and why?

Answer:

_____
_____
_____

Buy one, get one Free

No limit! Hurry! Offer expires soon!

QUESTION 6

A salon has an offer where a client can get a free bottle of shampoo worth £15, if they spend over £50. Another salon offers two free bottles of the same shampoo, if the client spends over £85. Which salon would you spend your money in and why?

Answer:

_____

_____

_____

_____

QUESTION 7

A salon has a special offer whereby if a client spends £50 they will receive a £10 voucher to purchase more goods at the same salon. If a client spends £200, how much money in vouchers could they expect to receive?

Answer:

_____

QUESTION 9

A salon offers shaving kits for £49.95 during the mid-year sale. A client purchases three as gifts and pays for them with 3 × £50 notes. What change is given?

Answer:

_____

QUESTION 8

A salon offers a special deal whereby if a client spends £100 they will receive a £15 voucher. A client purchases over £300 of goods. How much money in vouchers could they expect to receive?

Answer:

_____

QUESTION 10

Hair care products are on sale whereby if a client purchases two jars of hair gel for £19.95, they will get a third jar free. The client decides to purchase six jars of the product. How many will they end up with in total, considering the offer?

Answer:

_____

Unit 19: Industry Related Maths

Short-answer questions

Specific instructions to students

- This unit will allow you to practise a whole range of problem solving skills to work out industry related examples of calculations, deals, discounts, conversions and more.
- Read each question carefully and answer all of them in the spaces provided.
- You may not use a calculator.
- You need to show all working.

QUESTION 1

The Stock Control Card for 'Baked Meringue' styling product has gone missing and your manager, Jonno, wants you to complete a new one. You know that the initial order of 20 pump dispensers was received from the wholesalers on 1/3/11, and it was decided that this should be the maximum stock level, with the minimum stock level being four. Jonno also provided you with an invoice stating that he had ordered another 18 pump dispensers on 22/9/11, which were delivered on 27/9/11. He was not happy about the Stock Control Card going missing, as the salon had come close to running out of this product, as the stock had fallen below the agreed minimum stock level.

After checking with the stylists in the salon, you discover the following information:

Sue took 3 pump dispensers on 30/8/11

Sam took 3 pump dispensers on 3/3/11

Tyler took 1 pump dispenser on 7/4/11

Neil took 4 pump dispensers on 18/7/11

Wendy took 2 pump dispensers on 19/9/11

Tyler took another 3 pump dispensers on 30/5/11 and then another 1 pump dispenser on 1/6/11

a) Using the blank Stock Control Card, complete the details. You will have to rearrange the information in chronological order so that you maintain a record of stock level. Remember to read the introductory paragraph as this also includes details that will help you complete the Stock Control Card accurately.

Stock Control Card						
Stock Item			Maximum Stock Level		Minimum Stock Level	
Goods in	Date rec'd	Quantity issued	Date issued	Therapist's name	Stock level	Quantity and date reordered

b) What should Wendy have noticed on 19/9/11 and who should she have informed?

Answer

_____

_____

_____

QUESTION 2

Two stylists perform a series of services on two different clients; Lisa completes a cut, colour and finish, and Sasha completes a cut, perm and finish. Lisa starts her client at 9.37 a.m. and finishes at 11.44 a.m.; Emma starts her client at 9.42 a.m. and finishes at 11.17 a.m.

a) Who completes their client in the shortest time; Emma or Lisa?

Answer

_____

b) How long did Lisa take to complete her client?

Answer

_____

c) How long did Emma take to do her client?

Answer

_____

QUESTION 3

Kai places an order, via the Internet, with a national hair care company. Their delivery charges are priced according to the weight of the goods ordered. The weight of his order shows up on the checkout of the website as this image:

4.681 kg

a) What is the weight of his order, correct to the nearest kilogram?

Answer

_____

b) How much will Kai be charged for delivery, if the website states that delivery charges are as follows?

    A £5.95 for orders up to and including 4.5 kg

    B £6.50 for orders up to and including 7.5 kg

    C £8.95 for orders up to and including 10 kg

Answer

_____

QUESTION 4

Padma decides to place an order for some hair extension wefts from a German company's website. The prices stated are in euros. She checks the exchange rate is 0.9 euros to the pound (£).

a) What is 0.9 rounded to the nearest euro?

Answer

_____

b) Her order totals 378 euros. Padma wants to find the equivalent total in pounds sterling, so that she has an idea of how much money she is spending. How much, approximately, is Padma's order to the nearest pound (£)?

Answer

_____

QUESTION 5

Your salon manager asks you to find out how much it will cost to advertise in the local news paper, as they want to promote a special offer on hair care products.

a) You find out that the news paper charges £200 for a black and white advert and 30% more for a colour advert. How much extra would it be for a colour advert?

Answer

_____

b) The advert is to promote hair care products that are now 2/3 of the full price. The full price of a shampoo and conditioner duo pack is £21. What is the special promotion price of a shampoo and conditioner duo pack?

Answer

_____

c) This chart shows the number of shampoo and conditioner duo packs sold in the salon, in the month of December. What is the combined total of shampoo and conditioner duo packs sold in the weeks commencing 9 and 16 December?

Shampoo and conditioner duo packs sold in December	
w/c 2 December	⦀⦀
w/c 9 December	⦀⦀ II
w/c 16 December	⦀⦀ ⦀⦀ III
w/c 23 December	III
w/c 30 December	I

Answer

_____

QUESTION 6

Your salon hosts a Spring Fair to raise money for the local Hospice.

a) In total, you take £217 and have promised to donate 2/3 of the total to the local Hospice. Which calculation tells you how much money to give to the charity?

Answer

b) How much would the salon be able to donate to the Hospice?

Answer

QUESTION 7

Your salon organizes a Charity Hair, Make-up and Fashion Show. Money is raised through the sale of tickets to attend the Show, raffle tickets for sale on the evening and through local business donations.

a) The tickets cost £7.50 each. If 230 people attended the Show, how much was raised in total?

Answer

b) Raffle tickets were sold at the Show, costing £8 each. If 150 of the attendees bought one ticket each, how much money was raised through the sale of raffle tickets?

Answer

c) Ten local businesses also decide to support the Show by making a one-off monetary donation to add to the total raised.

The amounts are shown on this form. What is the **range** of the amounts paid?

Business	Amount (£)
Corner Newsagents	60
Kandy's Sweets	100
Mirabella Decor	100
Larry's Fish Bar	50
Handy Andy's DIY	10
Justine's Dezines	40
Just Pressed For Time	100
Four Seasons Restaurant	60
Malibu Bar	200
Dee's Dog Boutique	100

Answer

d) Using the previous table of monetary donations, what is the **mean** amount of the total given by the local businesses?

Answer

e) To cover the tables for the Show, you decide to buy some material. The material is sold by the metre, and 5 metres costs £17.50. How much would 9 metres cost?

Answer

QUESTION 8

As receptionist of a large hair salon, your manager has asked you to collect and present some data relating to the number of clients and their preferred service options. Through collecting these data and planning their presentation, you discover the following information:

a) At the reception you receive 44 clients in one day; 11 of these were men. What percentage of clients were men?

Answer

b) With regard to preferred service options, you collect data on four key services. What would be the best way to present these data so that they show each service as a share of the total?

Service	Numbers booked
Cut, style and finish	39%
Colour, style and finish	26%
Perm, style and finish	13%
Shampoo, style and finish	22%
	100%

Answer

c) Your manager asks you to continue collecting data on the same four key service options, over a period of 6 months. You produce the following table showing the sales of each service option purchased in July through to December.

Treatment Sales

	Perm, style and finish	Colour, style and finish	Cut, style and finish	Shampoo, style and finish	Total
July	47	29	63	65	204
August	48	40	84	86	258
September	37	57	81	55	230
October	59	73	82	67	281
November	30	97	86	43	256
December	19	86	97	62	264
Totals for 6 months	240	382	493	378	1,493

What is the **mean** monthly number of sales of 'Perm, style and finishes'?

Answer

_____

d) Your manager would also like you to choose a random sample of 20 clients and ask them to participate in a small survey to find out the time they took to travel to their appointment.

5 mins	45 mins	35 mins	35 mins	25 mins	55 mins	20 mins	25 mins	10 mins	25 mins
35 mins	10 mins	25 mins	40 mins	20 mins	45 mins	20 mins	15 mins	20 mins	35 mins

This chart shows the results in minutes. What percentage of journeys took longer than 30 minutes?

Answer

_____

QUESTION 9

A stylist needs to buy some hair gel. They find out the prices from four different suppliers. What is the **mean** price per pot of hair gel?

Salon Care	21st Century Hair	Hair Supplies	Hair Nation
£4.30	£4.80	£4.70	£4.20

Answer

_____

QUESTION 10

A stylist is mixing up two colours for a client; they have chosen to use 4 parts 'crimson promise' to 1 part 'maple syrup'. If they want to end up with 60 ml of hair colour, how much of the 'maple syrup' should they use?

Answer

_____

QUESTION 11

You have recently started a mobile hairdressing business and have decided to place an advert in the local newspaper. The news paper usually charges £80 for a full-page advert. However, they have agreed, as you are just starting up in business, to reduce the price to £32.

This gives you a saving of £48.

Which of the following options give the saving as a percentage of the normal price?

Answer

_____

QUESTION 12

The owner of a hairdressing salon has decided to sell their business premises through their local estate agents. They originally paid £100 000 for the premises and the estate agents have now put them on the market for £130 000.

The estate agents use the following formula to work out the percentage profit, $(S - O) \div O \times 100$, where S = selling price and O = original price.

What is the percentage profit?

Answer

_____

QUESTION 13

A stylist buys 103 bottles of shampoo and 103 bottles of conditioner at 95p per bottle.

Over a period of time, they sell 170 bottles for £3.55 a bottle.

How much profit will they have made?

Answer

_____

Unit 20:
Practice Written Exam for the Hairdressing Industry

Reading time: 10 minutes

Writing time: 1 hour 30 minutes

Section A: English

Section B: General Mathematics

Section C: Industry related Mathematics

QUESTION and ANSWER BOOK

Section	Topic	Number of questions	Marks
A	English	7	23
B	General Mathematics	11	25
C	Industry related Mathematics	34	52
		Total 52	Total 100

The sections may be completed in the order of your choice.

NO CALCULATORS are to be used during the exam.

Spelling

Read the passage below and then underline the 20 spelling errors.

10 marks

Gabrielle and Louise entered a hair salon and <u>desided</u> to have <u>diferent</u> styles. It was the end of the <u>shoping</u> day and they were keen to <u>spoill</u> themselves after a hard day in the <u>fashun</u> shops. Gabrielle chose to have a semi-permanent colour and Louise settled on having full-head foils. <u>Normaly</u>, the salon would be very <u>bussy</u> but the girls were lucky that there had been only a few <u>bokings</u> on this day. Everyone was <u>exsited</u>.

One <u>hairdreser</u> placed a cape over Louise and began to <u>prapare</u> her hair for the <u>foyles</u>. The hairdresser was <u>happry</u> to have a chat and <u>explaned</u> to Louise that she had a busy <u>weekend</u> planned. <u>Meenwhile</u>, Gabrielle was tended to by the other hairdresser who was also a keen <u>convasationalist</u>. Gabrielle had decided that she wanted a auburn <u>rince</u> as her hair colour and the hairdresser agreed that this would be a great look! Everything went <u>acording</u> to plan and the results turned out to be <u>wonderfull</u>. Both Gabrielle and Louise had enjoyed their visit to the salon and each was sporting different and stylish looks.

Correct the spelling errors by writing them out with the correct spelling below.

decided, different, shopping, spoil, fashion, normally, busy, bookings, excited, hairdresser, prepare, foils, happy,

explained, weekend, Meanwhile, conversationalist, rinse, according, wonderful

Alphabetizing

Put the following words into alphabetical order.

7 marks

regrowth	setting lotion
client	braiding
service	tinting
half-head foils	voucher
cutting comb	colour correction
blow-dry	thinning scissors
dimensional lift	human hair mannequin

blow-dry

braiding

client

colour correction

cutting comb

dimensional lift

half-head foils
_____

human hair mannequin
_____

regrowth
_____

service
_____

setting lotion
_____

thinning scissors
_____

tint
_____

voucher
_____

Comprehension

Short-answer questions

Specific instructions to students

- Read the following passage and answer the questions below.

> Paul and Maria started work at the local hair salon centre at 9.00 a.m. on a Thursday. There was late-night shopping and both knew it was going to be a long day as one of the other hairdressers had called in ill. Thursday nights were always popular for families and students and, with students going back to school in a week, Paul felt that this could be one of their busiest working days. He decided to ring Jamie and ask him to help out. Unfortunately, Jamie was unavailable as he was travelling to Manchester for the weekend. Luckily, Amber was available and left for the salon straightaway, arriving at 9.25 a.m. Soon after, the first clients began to arrive. Paul's first client was a man who required a cut and finish. Maria's first client was a young lady who had short hair and wanted a half-head of foils. Amber's first client arrived less than 5 minutes later and the client wanted a wash, cut and blow-dry.
>
> By midday, everything had been moving along smoothly. Paul had completed eight cut and styles, Maria had been kept busy with working on foils as well as putting a semi-colour through two client's hair and Amber had completed nine wash, cut and blow-dry treatments. Paul took his lunch break first, followed by Maria then Amber. They needed to stagger the breaks so that there were at least two hairdressers in the salon at all times. The rest of the day was very prosperous for the salon. By closing time, the salon had takings in the till well over the norm for a Thursday's trading. Paul was so excited that he treated Maria and Amber to dinner and drinks at a local restaurant.

QUESTION 1   1 mark

What time did the salon open on the Thursday?

Answer:

The salon opened at 9.00 a.m.
_____

QUESTION 2   1 mark

Why did Paul feel that this was going to be one of their busiest days?

Answer:

Thursday nights are popular with families and students.

School would also be starting again in a week.

QUESTION 3   1 mark

What did each hairdresser's first client want as their hair treatment?

Answer:

Paul's first client required a cut and finish.

Maria's first client wanted a half-head of foils.

Amber's first client wanted a wash,

cut and blow-dry.

QUESTION 4   1 mark

By midday, what treatments had each hairdresser completed?

Answer:

Paul had completed eight cut and styles. Maria had

completed doing foils and semi-colours for two clients.

Amber had completed nine wash, cut and blow-dry

treatments.

QUESTION 5   2 marks

Why did Paul choose to stagger their breaks?

Answer:

Paul chose to stagger their breaks so that there would

always be at least two hairdressers in the salon.

Section B: General Mathematics

QUESTION 1   1 + 1 + 1 = 3 marks

What unit of measurement would you use to measure:

a) The length of a hair extension?

Answer:

Centimetres or inches

b) The temperature of a sterilizer?

Answer:

Degrees Celsius

c) The amount of liquid hair colour?

Answer:

Millilitres or litres

QUESTION 2   1 + 1 + 1 = 3 marks

Write an example of the following and give an instance of where it may be found in the hairdressing industry:

a) Percentages

Answer:

A sale discount

b) Decimals

Answer:

Prices

c) Fractions

Answer:

Quarter-head foils

QUESTION 3   1 + 1 = 2 marks

Convert the following units:

a) 1 kg to grams

Answer:

1000 g

b) 1500 g to kilograms

Answer:

1.5 kg

QUESTION 4   1 mark

Write the following in descending order:

0.7   0.71   7.1   70.1   701.00   7.0

Answer:

701.00, 70.1, 7.1, 7.0, 0.71, 0.7

QUESTION 5   1 + 1 = 2 marks

Write the decimal number that is between the
following:

a) 0.1 and 0.2

Answer:

0.15

b) 1.3 and 1.4

Answer:

1.35

QUESTION 6   1 + 1 = 2 marks

Round off the following numbers to two decimal
places:

a) 5.177

Answer:

5.18

b) 12.655

Answer:

12.66

QUESTION 7   1 + 1 = 2 marks

Calculate the following to the nearest whole number:

a) 101 × 81 =

Answer:

8000

b) 399 × 21 =

Answer:

8000

QUESTION 8   1 + 1 = 2 marks

What do the following add up to?

a) £25, £13.50 and £165.50

Answer:

£204

b) £4, £5.99 and £229.50

Answer:

£239.49

QUESTION 9   1 + 1 = 2 marks

Subtract the following:

a) 196 from 813

Answer:

617

b) 5556 from 9223

Answer:

3667

QUESTION 10   1 + 1 = 2 marks

Use division to solve:

a) 4824 ÷ 3 =

Answer:

1608

b) 84.2 ÷ 0.4 =

Answer:

210.5

QUESTION 11   2 + 2 = 4 marks

Using the acronym BODMAS, solve:

a) (3 × 7) × 4 + 9 − 5 =

Answer:

88

b) (8 × 12) × 2 + 8 − 4 =

Answer:

196

Section C: Industry related Mathematics

Basic Operations

Addition

A salon purchases 36 bottles of shampoo, 144 capes or gowns and 15 vent brushes. How many items have been purchased in total?

Answer:

195

A hairdresser completes three cuts charging £25, £45 and £17. How much has been charged in total?

Answer:

£87

Subtraction

A salon uses 57 foils from a box that contains 150 foils. How many remain?

Answer:

93

A client purchases hair care products and the total comes to £124. The manager takes off a discount of £35 during a sale. How much does the client pay?

Answer:

£89

Multiplication

A salon purchases four deluxe salon stools for £124 each, two shampoo basins for £635 each and three mannequin heads costing £32 each. What is the total cost?

Answer:

£1862

A salon purchases 5.5 inch hairdressing scissors with cases. If one pair costs £23, how much will eight pairs cost?

Answer:

£184

Division

The week's takings for a salon are £3155. If the salon was open for 6 days, what would be the average takings per day?

Answer:

£525.83

At an annual stocktake at a salon, the receptionist counts 72 bottles of conditioner. If 12 bottles are packed into each box, how many boxes are there?

Answer:

6

Decimals

Addition

A client buys the following hair care products from a salon: a can of hair spray for £19.95, some hair gel for £9.50 and a set of hair brushes for £34.50. How much for the purchases in total?

Answer:

£63.95

A salon has clients who need hairdressing services in the lead-up to the festive season. The cost for one service is £39.50, another is £43.50 and a third service is £21.50. How much is the total for all three?

Answer:

£104.50

Subtraction

QUESTION 1   1 mark

An apprentice works 38 hours and earns £418.50. He spends £55.95 on clothes and £25.00 on a mobile phone top-up. How much is left?

Answer:

£337.55

QUESTION 2   1 mark

A three-bar footrest is purchased for a salon at a cost of £24.50. If it is paid for with a £50 note from the float, how much change will be given?

Answer:

£25.50

Multiplication

QUESTION 1   1 + 1 = 2 marks

A hairdresser goes to a wholesaler where tubs of hair gel are priced at £14.95.

a) How much does it cost for three tubs?

Answer:

£44.85

b) What is the change from £50?

Answer:

£5.15

QUESTION 2   1 + 1 = 2 marks

Four hairdressing equipment trolleys are purchased at a cost of £148.50 each.

a) What is the total of this purchase?

Answer:

£594

b) What is the change from £600.00?

Answer:

£6

Division

QUESTION 1   1 mark

A salon has takings of £1455.00 over 12 hours for a Thursday's trading. How much does this work out to be, on average, per hour?

Answer:

£121.25

QUESTION 2   2 marks

Four clients have hair services. The total for all four clients comes to £76.80. What is the cost to each client, assuming they all have the same cut?

Answer:

£19.20

Fractions

QUESTION 1   1 mark

$\frac{1}{4} + \frac{1}{2} =$

Answer:

$\frac{3}{4}$

QUESTION 2   1 mark

$\frac{4}{5} - \frac{1}{3} =$

Answer:

$\frac{7}{15}$

QUESTION 3   1 mark

$\frac{2}{3} \times \frac{1}{4} =$

Answer:

$\frac{1}{6}$

QUESTION 4   1 mark

$\frac{3}{4} \div \frac{1}{2} =$

Answer:

$1\frac{1}{2}$

Percentages

QUESTION 1   1 + 1 = 2 marks

A salon has a '10% off' sale on all items. If a client purchases items totalling £149, what is the final sale price?

Answer:

£134.10

QUESTION 2   1 + 1 + 1 = 3 marks

Hair care products are discounted by 20%. The regular retail price of certain products comes to £120.

a) How much is the discount worth?

Answer:

£24

b) What is the price of the products after the discount?

Answer:

£96

c) How much change would be needed if a £100 note was used to pay for the products?

Answer:

£4

Measurement Conversions

QUESTION 1   2 marks

How many grams are there in 1.85 kg?

Answer:

1850 g

QUESTION 2   2 marks

35 mm converts to how many centimetres?

Answer:

3.5 cm

Area

QUESTION 1   2 marks

The floor area of a salon measures 15 m by 6 m. What is the total floor area?

Answer:

90 m²

QUESTION 2   2 marks

What is the total window area that measures 2.2 m by 1.5 m and displays hair care products?

Answer:

3.3 m²

Earning Wages

QUESTION 1   2 marks

A part-time hairdresser gets paid £12.50 per hour. If he works 15 hours a week, how much will be his gross pay?

Answer:

£187.50

QUESTION 2   2 marks

A hairdresser spends the following time on five different clients: 17 minutes, 35 minutes, 19 minutes, 48 minutes and 58 minutes respectively.

a) How much time, in minutes, has been taken?

Answer:

177 minutes

b) How much time, in hours and minutes, has been taken?

Answer:

2 hours and 57 minutes

Squaring Numbers

QUESTION 1   2 marks

What is 7^2?

Answer:

49

QUESTION 2   2 marks

The floor area of a warehouse measures 13 m × 13 m. What is the total floor area?

Answer:

169 m²

Vouchers

QUESTION 1   2 marks

A client walks into a salon with a '20% off' voucher. If £148.60 worth of products are purchased, what will be the final cost to the client once the voucher is used?

Answer:

£118.88

A client purchases goods to the total of £78.60. A voucher for '15% off' is then produced. How much is charged after the voucher is used?

Answer:

£66.81

Deals

QUESTION 1   2 marks

A salon has bottles of shampoo on special offer for £14.95, or you can buy two for £26. Which is the better deal and how much, if any, will be saved?

Answer:

The better deal is two for £26, as this works out to be

£13 per bottle. This is a saving of £1.95 per bottle.

QUESTION 2   2 marks

A salon sells a bottle of mousse for £9.50 or three for £27. Which is the better deal and how much, if any, will be saved?

Answer:

The better deal is three for £27, as this works out to be

£9 per bottle. This is a saving of 50 pence per bottle.

Hairdressing Glossary

Activators Products used to maintain curl in permed or naturally curly hair.

Bob Classic look of the 1950s and 1960s. The style is short and straight but blow-dried and curled under.

Chemically treated hair Hair that has been either relaxed, permed or coloured or has undergone any mixture of these processes.

Colour test A test to ascertain if a colour is suitable and/or achievable. It can be done on a test cutting or on a small section of hair on the head.

Conditioner Creamy hair product meant to be used after shampoo. Moisturizes and detangles hair.

Confidential information May include personal aspects of conversations with clients, personal aspects of conversations with colleagues, contents of client records, client and staff personal details (e.g. addresses and telephone numbers, etc.) financial aspects of the business, gossip.

Contra-indications Conditions which indicate a service should not be carried out.

Density The amount of hair follicles in a given area.

Disinfection Inhibits the growth of disease causing microorganisms (except spores) using chemical agents.

Effleurage A gentle stroking movement.

Erythema Abnormal skin redness resulting from increased blood flow to the skin which can be caused by infection, massage, electrical treatment, allergies, exercise or injury to the tissue.

Elasticity test A test to check the strength of the internal structure of the hair.

Feathering A cutting technique hairdressers use to take hard lines out of the hair. By cutting into the hair, soft lines can be created.

Foils A highlighting method that incorporates selecting strands of hair and applying colour to add visual interest to hair.

Fringe The front section of hair that creates a frame for your face; can be one of the most important parts of a hairstyle.

Friction A vigorous rubbing movement using the finger pads. It is stimulating rather than relaxing and is not always carried out. It is only done for a few minutes, working from front to back.

Full-head application of permanent colour and/or lightener This technique generally requires the separate application to mid-lengths, ends and the roots as part of the same process to achieve a colour change.

Gown Lightweight, waterproof, adjustable, protective item that is placed over the front of the client and adjusted around the neck.

Graduation The build up of a shape. It can create a curve in the hair and is the opposite of layering.

Hair extensions Pieces of real or synthetic hair weaved close to the scalp in order to achieve greater length and/or fullness.

Hair growth patterns These are double crown, widows peak, cow lick, nape whorl, natural parting and regrowth.

Highlights A colouring process for particular strands of hair that can give your hair brighter effects and add volume to certain types of hair.

Incompatibility This refers to chemicals which do not work together and may have an adverse reaction.

Layering A technique used by hairdressers to make hair appear thinner or thicker.

Legal requirements This refers to laws affecting the way businesses are operated, how the salon or workplace is set up and maintained, people in employment and the systems of working which must be maintained. Of particular importance are the COSHH Regulations, the Electricity at Work Regulations and the Cosmetic Products (Safety) Regulations.

Lighteners Products that lighten the natural pigments of the hair (changes melanin and pheomelanin to oxymelanin) without depositing artificial colour – otherwise known as bleach or pre-lighteners.

Makeover Total change of style.

Mousse An aerosol foam used in hair styling.

Manufacturers' instructions Explicit guidance issued by manufacturers or suppliers of products or equipment, concerning their safe and efficient use.

Microorganisms   Organisms of microscopic size.

Natural hair   Hair which still has its **natural** structure, be it tightly or loosely coiled. This term is used in relation to African type hair.

Normalizing products   These are post-relaxing treatments and shampoos. They are sometimes also known as 'stabilisers' or 'neutralizing' products for the relaxing process.

Oxidizing agents   These products introduce oxygen into the hair. They are mixed with oxidation based colour removers, colouring and lightening products and used in neutralizers.

Perm   Curls, generally long-lasting, created by restructuring the hair molecules with a chemical or heat treatment.

Partial head colour   This may apply to areas of the head and could include techniques such as slices, block colour, polishing/shoeshining, woven or pull-through highlights and lowlights, etc.

Personal Protective Equipment (PPE)   You are required to use and wear the appropriate protective equipment or clothing during colouring, perming and relaxing services. Protective gloves and apron are the normal requirement for yourself.

Petrissage   Slow, firm, kneading movement.

Porosity   The speed at which hair can absorb moisture and or liquid. This is dependent on the condition of the hair cuticle.

Pulled-through highlights and lowlights   This technique can include the use of a variety of commercially available products (e.g. colour pots, plastic/rubber caps, bags, plastic strips, spatulas, etc.).

Quasi permanent colour   Colouring products which should be treated as permanent colours in terms of testing and future services. These products are mixed with oxidizers, e.g. low strength hydrogen peroxide (developers) and are normally expected to last up to 12 shampoos, depending on the porosity of the hair.

Rotary   A firm circular movement using the pads of the fingers over the surface of the scalp.

Semi-permanent   A colour which lasts from 6–8 shampoos.

Sensitized hair   Hair which has a fragile internal structure naturally OR caused by mechanical, chemical and/or environmental factors.

Serum   A silicone based product used for styling.

Sharps   A term used by the Health and Safety Executive to describe sharp objects. In the context of hairdressing sharps include scissors, razors and razor blades which may have bye-laws covering their disposal.

Skin test   A test to determine if the client is allergic to the product being applied.

Sterilization   The total destruction of microorganisms.

Strand test   This test is used in colouring, lightening, rearranging and relaxing processes to establish the effect of the product on the hair and its condition i.e.

For Colouring: the depth and tone has been achieved.

For Lightening: the degree of lift has been achieved.

For Rearranging: the degree of straightness has been achieved before winding.

For Relaxing: the degree of straightness has been achieved.

Tensile strength test   A test to determine the breaking point of hair which indicates the strength of the internal structure of the hair.

Texturizer   A treatment left on the hair for a short period of time that slightly relaxes the natural curl of hair.

Tint   A permanent colour.

Tint brush   Used to apply tints from a bowl.

Treatment   Used between shampoo and conditioner to put protein back into hair.

Toner (colour)   The use of pastel or fantasy colourants to enhance the effect of a permanent colour or lightener result.

Tapotement   A stimulating movement which consists of light tapping and patting on the face and scalp.

Trichologist   A trichologist is academically trained in the biology and disorders of the hair and scalp. Trichologists are able to advise on, diagnose conditions, often with the use of a microscope to treat a wide range of hair loss and hair and scalp problems. They may also have the knowledge and skills to prescribe and blend specialist pharmaceutical preparations.

Virgin hair   Hair that has not had any chemical treatment on it.

Weaving (colour)   Applying colour to woven sections of hair.

Wefts   Temporary hair extensions which are fixed into your hair.

Maths and English Glossary

Adjectives   Describes things, people and places, such as 'sharp', 'warm' or 'handsome'

Adverbs   Describes the way something happens, such as 'slowly', 'often' or 'quickly'

Homophones   Words that sound the same, but are spelt differently and have different meanings

Nouns   Names of things, people and places, such as 'chair', 'George' or 'Sheffield'

Pronouns   Short words like 'it', 'you', 'we' or 'they', etc. used instead of actual names

Ratio   A way to compare the amounts of something

Verbs   Words to describe what you are 'doing', such as 'to mix', 'smile/frown' or 'walking'

Formulae and Data

Circumference of a Circle

$C = \pi \times d$

where: C = circumference, π = 3.14, d = diameter

Diameter of a Circle

$d = \frac{C}{\pi}$

where: C = circumference, π = 3.14, d = diameter

Area

$A = l \times b$

Area = length × breadth and is given in square units

Volume of a Cube

$V = l \times w \times h$

Volume = length × width × height and is given in cubic units

Volume of a Cylinder

$V_c = \pi \times r^2 \times h$

where: V_c = volume of a cylinder, π = 3.14, r = radius, h = height

Times Tables

1

1 × 1	=	1
2 × 1	=	2
3 × 1	=	3
4 × 1	=	4
5 × 1	=	5
6 × 1	=	6
7 × 1	=	7
8 × 1	=	8
9 × 1	=	9
10 × 1	=	10
11 × 1	=	11
12 × 1	=	12

2

1 × 2	=	2
2 × 2	=	4
3 × 2	=	6
4 × 2	=	8
5 × 2	=	10
6 × 2	=	12
7 × 2	=	14
8 × 2	=	16
9 × 2	=	18
10 × 2	=	20
11 × 2	=	22
12 × 2	=	24

3

1 × 3	=	3
2 × 3	=	6
3 × 3	=	9
4 × 3	=	12
5 × 3	=	15
6 × 3	=	18
7 × 3	=	21
8 × 3	=	24
9 × 3	=	27
10 × 3	=	30
11 × 3	=	33
12 × 3	=	36

4

1 × 4	=	4
2 × 4	=	8
3 × 4	=	12
4 × 4	=	16
5 × 4	=	20
6 × 4	=	24
7 × 4	=	28
8 × 4	=	32
9 × 4	=	36
10 × 4	=	40
11 × 4	=	44
12 × 4	=	48

5

1 × 5	=	5
2 × 5	=	10
3 × 5	=	15
4 × 5	=	20
5 × 5	=	25
6 × 5	=	30
7 × 5	=	35
8 × 5	=	40
9 × 5	=	45
10 × 5	=	50
11 × 5	=	55
12 × 5	=	60

6

1 × 6	=	6
2 × 6	=	12
3 × 6	=	18
4 × 6	=	24
5 × 6	=	30
6 × 6	=	36
7 × 6	=	42
8 × 6	=	48
9 × 6	=	54
10 × 6	=	60
11 × 6	=	66
12 × 6	=	72

7

1 × 7	=	7
2 × 7	=	14
3 × 7	=	21
4 × 7	=	28
5 × 7	=	35
6 × 7	=	42
7 × 7	=	49
8 × 7	=	56
9 × 7	=	63
10 × 7	=	70
11 × 7	=	77
12 × 7	=	84

8

1 × 8	=	8
2 × 8	=	16
3 × 8	=	24
4 × 8	=	32
5 × 8	=	40
6 × 8	=	48
7 × 8	=	56
8 × 8	=	64
9 × 8	=	72
10 × 8	=	80
11 × 8	=	88
12 × 8	=	96

9

1 × 9	=	9
2 × 9	=	18
3 × 9	=	27
4 × 9	=	36
5 × 9	=	45
6 × 9	=	54
7 × 9	=	63
8 × 9	=	72
9 × 9	=	81
10 × 9	=	90
11 × 9	=	99
12 × 9	=	108

10

1 × 10	=	10
2 × 10	=	20
3 × 10	=	30
4 × 10	=	40
5 × 10	=	50
6 × 10	=	60
7 × 10	=	70
8 × 10	=	80
9 × 10	=	90
10 × 10	=	100
11 × 10	=	110
12 × 10	=	120

11

1 × 11	=	11
2 × 11	=	22
3 × 11	=	33
4 × 11	=	44
5 × 11	=	55
6 × 11	=	66
7 × 11	=	77
8 × 11	=	88
9 × 11	=	99
10 × 11	=	110
11 × 11	=	121
12 × 11	=	132

12

1 × 12	=	12
2 × 12	=	24
3 × 12	=	36
4 × 12	=	48
5 × 12	=	60
6 × 12	=	72
7 × 12	=	84
8 × 12	=	96
9 × 12	=	108
10 × 12	=	120
11 × 12	=	132
12 × 12	=	144

Multiplication Grid

	1	2	3	4	5	6	7	8	9	10	11	12
1	1	2	3	4	5	6	7	8	9	10	11	12
2	2	4	6	8	10	12	14	16	18	20	22	24
3	3	6	9	12	15	18	21	24	27	30	33	36
4	4	8	12	16	20	24	28	32	36	40	44	48
5	5	10	15	20	25	30	35	40	45	50	55	60
6	6	12	18	24	30	36	42	48	54	60	66	72
7	7	14	21	28	35	42	49	56	63	70	77	84
8	8	16	24	32	40	48	56	64	72	80	88	96
9	9	18	27	36	45	54	63	72	81	90	99	108
10	10	20	30	40	50	60	70	80	90	100	110	120
11	11	22	33	44	55	66	77	88	99	110	121	132
12	12	24	36	48	60	72	84	96	108	120	132	144

Maths and English for Hairdressing
Online Answer Guide

To access the Answer Guide for Maths and English for Hairdressing follow these simple steps:

1) Copy the following link into your web browser:

http://www.cengagebrain.co.uk/shop/isbn/9781408072677

2) Click on the Free Study Tools Link.

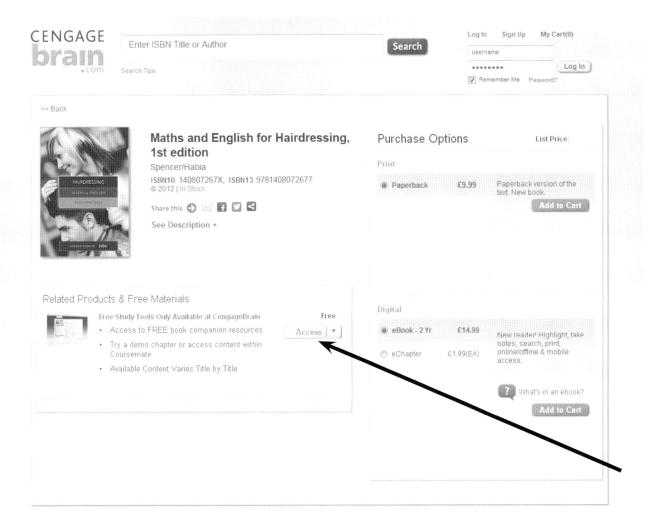

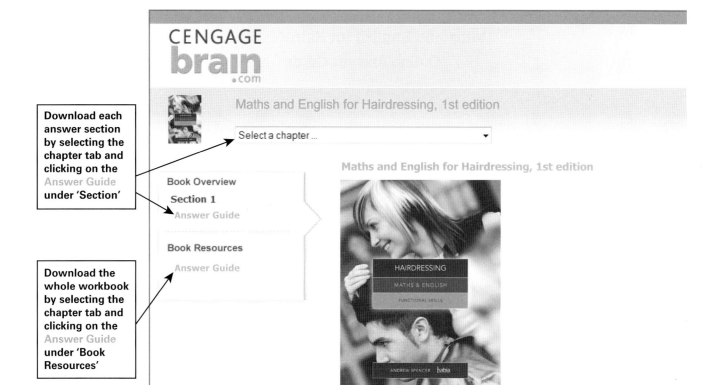

Download each answer section by selecting the chapter tab and clicking on the Answer Guide **under 'Section'**

Download the whole workbook by selecting the chapter tab and clicking on the Answer Guide **under 'Book Resources'**

CENGAGE
brain
.com

Maths and English for Hairdressing, 1st edition

Select a chapter ...

Book Overview

Section 1

Answer Guide

Book Resources

Answer Guide

Maths and English for Hairdressing, 1st edition

HAIRDRESSING

MATHS & ENGLISH

FUNCTIONAL SKILLS

ANDREW SPENCER   habia